IT'S A

WRITTEN AND ILLUST

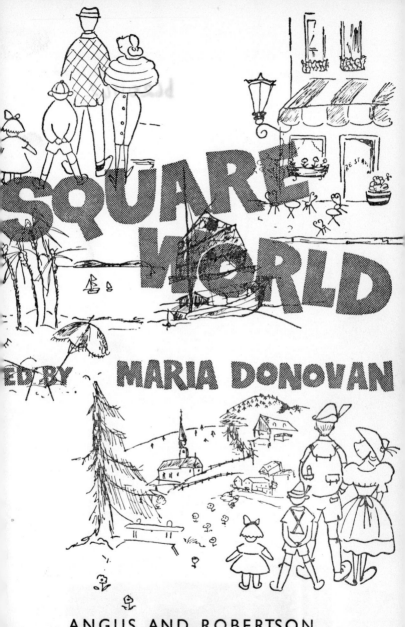

SQUARE WORLD

ED BY MARIA DONOVAN

ANGUS AND ROBERTSON

First published by F. W. Cheshire, Melbourne,
this edition first published by Angus & Robertson Ltd., London, 1962

b6201142

To

Daisy

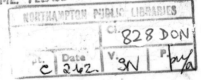
PRINTED IN AUSTRALIA BY HALSTEAD PRESS, SYDNEY
Registered in Australia for transmission by post as a book

The Waldorf-Astoria

NEW YORK

Master Paddy Donovan,
71 Stevenson Street,
Kew,
Melbourne,
Australia

My dear Paddy,

Before you discover it, let me explain what happened. You see, it's obvious that I plagiarised. (Kindly look "plagiarised" up in Dad's *Oxford Dictionary*—no time to explain what it means now.) This was your book. Your ideas, your words. All I did was write it down and send it to the publishers as if it was my work.

I'll promise to buy you that train for Christmas. Also the cowboy suit. Anything else you want, let me know. Only, please, don't sue me when you are twenty-one. The royalties would have been spent by then, anyhow.

Your ever-loving

Mum.

CONTENTS

1 *Mr. Carnegie is not a Hungarian*

My mother is Hungarian. My Dad's a Professor. I guess I don't mind. Really, I don't. I used to when I was a kid. When I was in Grade One. Now I am in Grade Three and I have my Outlook. I am kind of broadminded. But when I was a kid it was awful. Mum used to pick me up at school and she did not wear a hat. Also, she could never say "What?" She always said "Vat?" This is because Hungarians can't say a W. It's horrible. Otherwise poor Mum's OK. Only, she never comes to the mothers' meeting. I guess she's probably ashamed that she cannot say What. Or maybe she doesn't want to buy a hat. She wears a chignon. I wish she didn't.

One day, when I am still in Grade One, Dad says to us, OK, we'll go around the world. He has this Grant, he says. I know he has no money, because we have just bought this big house here around the corner. So I guess Grant must be the same as money. A man called Carnegie gave it to Dad. At least he is not a Hungarian.

So we go around the world. It takes us a year. This is because of Daisy. She is my sister. Mum says we must take it slowly because of Daisy. Otherwise, I bet we could have done it in a day. But Daisy is a drag. She is three when we start off. I wish we could leave her with Granny. I tell her she can have my electric train without the engine if she stayed home with Granny. But she starts to perform. I say she can have my bike without the back wheel, and she screams. So I give her a good smack on her fat bottom. Daisy has the fattest bottom in the world. She says she is coming with us, because she wants a mink stole. Honest. She's a funny kid. Clothes, clothes, clothes. That's all there is on her mind. And cakes. She has absolutely no Outlook. When we get back from our trip, she is as dumb as ever. But we had to get this extra suitcase to put her clothes in —what she collected all over the world. People buy clothes for Daisy because they say she is so cute when she models them. I think she just has a fat bottom, and that's that. And no Outlook. She's a show-off too. Just because she can speak Schwyzerdütsch and Italian she thinks she's smart. OK. That's all about Daisy. I wouldn't be surprised if she grew up a Hungarian.

So Dad takes this Grant and buys the tickets and we fly off to Sydney. It's only a minute to fly to Sydney because we live in Melbourne, Australia. I am quite used to flying because when I was a kid I flew a lot. I flew from Adelaide, Australia, to Melbourne, Australia. That was when Mum went to Japan to buy herself a kimono. (Gosh, she looks awful in that kimono too, but I don't mind, because Mum's really OK, only she can't help it that she was born different from us.)

The plane we take in Sydney is very big. There is an overnight bag for me, Paddy. Daisy has one too, but Mum stuffs hers full with her manuscripts. You see, Mum wants to be a writer. She wrote these six novels and two cookery books. All she needs now is to find somebody to print it and make it into books.

I put a few basic toys into my overnight bag, but Mum throws them out promptly and fills the bag with her shoes. Six pairs of them. They weigh a ton. When I say so, Dad says, Paddy, shut up. Do you expect your mother to go barefoot around the world? What would the Hungarians say?

Anyway, we get on this plane and the hostess smiles, and the Captain smiles at Mum, and Daisy, of course, wiggles her fat bottom. She's kind of crazy about men

2

and thinks the Captain is smiling at her. And what happens next is really not too bad at all. Because, as we are looking for our seats, Dad goes with Mum and sits right in the back, ten rows away from us. I am very happy, because this means that people will really think that we are on our own. No Mum. No Dad. I wish I wouldn't have to sit beside Daisy, but one cannot have everything in this life.

So I tell Daisy to pretend that we are orphans. When people ask—Little boy, little girl, where is your Mummy?—we'll just look sad. They will feel sorry for us then and give us candy. It's very easy to fool grown-ups, I explain to Daisy, because they have no experience of what it is to be kids. They believe everything you tell them.

Of course, Daisy almost ruins everything. Because as soon as the plane takes off, she begins to bawl, Mummy, Mummy! I want to make veeeeeee . . . It's lucky that Mum and Dad pretend to be asleep. They don't hear Daisy, because their eyes are closed. Everybody else hears her, of course. At last the nun in the seat behind her leans forward and asks, What's the matter, darling? Have you lost your Mummy?

I don't trust Daisy to say the right thing, so I answer myself. We have no Mummy, I say. She died. She was very old and got drowned in the bath. And our Daddy's dead too. He had a brain-storm. His brain burst, and next he was cold and dead.

The nun looks real sad behind her glasses. She reaches into her black bag and gives me a holy picture. Then she searches around a bit more and comes up with a lolly-pop for Daisy. That lucky pig. And to think that it is me who has to take her out to the toilet in the end.

When we get back to our seats, I want a little peace

and quiet. So I just sit there and look out of the window. I think of things like Father Christmas and the angels and God. One kind of believes there is such a thing as Father Christmas and the angels when one looks out of a plane. All these clouds, which are really not clouds at all, but nice puffs of fairy-floss and magic. I bet if I got out of the plane right now, I could walk on top of these clouds until I came to God's palace. He has a beautiful palace all made of diamonds and precious stones and fairy-floss clouds for curtains.

This is why I like flying. You get ideas and you can make-believe for hours. Naturally, whenever I fly I wear my school uniform, with the maroon-blue-and-yellow stripes on my tie and socks. This way people can tell straight away that I go to the University. Which is exactly the place I go to school. Dad takes me in the car every morning. They call our school Teachers' Training College, and Mr. Viney is our master. We are very precious and rare. They call us experiments. And, of course, Experiment Number One is me, Paddy, because my Dad's a Professor. You see, Mr. Viney tries to tell me that it makes no difference my Dad being a Professor. But I know it does.

When we leave Australia on this trip it's winter. August and winter. Daisy travels in my old overcoat. She looks like a dwarf in it, with the sleeves coming right down to her knees and the coat just about hiding her sausage-ankles. Granny, who sees us off at the airport, says to Mum, who is her daughter: Aren't you ashamed of yourself to take these kids around the world dressed like poor peasants? I ask Granny what a peasant is, but she ignores me. Fixing her eyes on Mum, she asks —Veeell? Which is English, and means Well?

Mum says, First comes first, and as it is I couldn't afford a wardrobe for every one of us. What's more, look at this suit I am wearing! It's two years old. Nevertheless, Granny isn't happy about the way we look. So I ask Dad what a peasant is, but Dad's busy being polite to Granny, which I know is hard on his nerves. He wants to make a last-minute happy impression on Granny, and so when we get on the plane, I am left in ignorance.

I get up and walk down the aisle pretending to be thirsty, but really what I want is to find out what a peasant is. Dad, whom I ask, opens one eye just a little

bit and says, Don't worry, Paddy. Your Granny is typically feudal. Then he goes back to pretend to sleep.

So when I come back to my place, I feel it's time to start a little conversation with that nun in the seat behind us. Maybe if I talk real nice and educated she will give me a lolly-pop too. Which is why I turn around and ask her, Excuse me, please, what does feudal mean?

6

Well, her eyes nearly pop out of her glasses. She says something very long and complicated, like something of a something of a system. I don't understand it, which is why I say very politely, Thank you very much, now I know what my Granny is! I think she must be pleased with my nice manners because she laughs a lot. I am sure she wants to give me a lolly-pop but just this moment Daisy butts in, and begins to tell this nun that we have a new house. It's really an old house, she says, but we did it over, and we put a *bidet* in the bathroom and a chandelier in the toyroom.

I am furious, but I can't help admitting that that kid can talk real well, if she wants to. Nobody believes her when she says she's only three, which shows that she is really a show-off. She also explains to that nun that we haven't paid for our house yet, because we have no money, only debts. Whereupon this same nun crosses herself and starts to click her rosary beads. And there's no lolly-pop for me, to be sure.

The next moment the plane touches the ground and we are in Fiji.

2 *The Foot that made Fiji worth seeing*

Fɪᴊɪ is very dark. And hot. When we come off the plane we can't see a thing. It must be well past our bed-time, since I hear Mum say, Vat—they expect us to have breakfast at midnight?

In the rest-house we sit down to a table and I help myself to a couple of bottles of orange-soda. Meanwhile we lose Daisy. Mum yells, For heaven's sake where did you leave that child? and Dad jumps up and goes from table to table, hoping to find the kid. I could help him, I could, but I prefer to stay incognito and have another orange-soda and a double ice-cream.

You see, Daisy likes the Captain so much that she goes and sits with him and the crew. Besides, they are having gin-and-tonic and Martinis and there's nothing Daisy likes more than the olive from a dry Martini. When Dad discovers her, she is just a little bit drunk and curls up under our table and goes to sleep.

There isn't much to Fiji, I can tell you. At night it's dark there, and you can get a good curry, if you like the stuff. I personally don't. Outside the rest-house they have these funny torches and a gramophone which plays "I gotta get that guy right out of my hair". It's maybe different when you land in Fiji at day-time. To be sure they wouldn't have these torches and the gramophone may play my favourite—"O what a beautiful morning".

The most interesting thing in Fiji was that foot. I only remembered it much later, when one day in Central Park, New York, Daisy began to babble about a foot in Fiji.

It was a foot, very big, nice, black and without shoes

8

on it. It belonged to one of the waiters, who carried the drinks around. Not an ordinary foot either. Because right there between its Big and Second Toe a red flower wobbled with every step. The kind of flower ladies wear on their hats. But that one decorated the foot, and it was very interesting.

You learn something every place you go to. Nowadays, when I think of Fiji, I take off my shoes, put a rose between my toes and practise my elegant walk.

3 *I fall in love with her water-skis*

WHEN you fly at night, you can see the sparks firing backwards from the engines. Like crackers they seem, No. 2 Special Chinese Fire Crackers which cost sixpence each. We let them off on Guy Fawkes' night in Melbourne.

Mostly, however, they make you sleep at night on the plane. I know kids whom I met around the world and they tell me their Mum gives them dope. My Mum never gives us dope to put us to sleep. She is a bad sport.

Instead, she makes up a bed for Daisy on the floor, right under my seat. If there is somebody else sitting beside me, Mum asks him, Would you kindly give up your seat so that my little son could stretch out? By this time, whoever sat beside me is glad to give up his seat even if he has to stand. We get into our pyjamas and go to bed in the air. Sounds silly.

You miss so much in your geography on account of these sleeps. For instance, we have just left Fiji, went to bed, and next thing is, there was the sign flashing, Fasten Your Seat Belts, and we were down in Honolulu.

Honolulu is the place I meet Gwendy.

She wears a mess of flowers around her neck which she says are leis. I know they aren't. They are orchids. Mum has a friend who grows them under glass.

Gwendy gives us each a lot of orchids to put around our necks, and she kisses me. She also gives me a box of chocolates and five lolly-pops. And a frog to Daisy, but it died the next day.

Gwendy's Mum and my Mum were room-mates in Chicago. That was once upon a time. Yet they still call each other Kiddo, I mean Auntie Patsy and Mum. I wish only my Mum would not have this loud voice which makes people turn around and look at her when she shouts Kiddo! to Gwendy's Mum, who's Japanese and a Senator.

Gwendy can dance the hula which is easy. All you need is a grass skirt, a flower in your hair and a gramophone with a handle which plays Old Mother Hubbard. You wiggle your hips and screw up your eyes, pretending you are Old Mother Hubbard getting a bone for her poor doggy. You see, hula-hula is not dancing, but acting out a story. You can do Humpty-Dumpty too, if you like. Main thing is to wear this grass skirt and no shoes on your feet so you can wiggle your toes too.

I don't know why, but I guess I fell in love with Gwendy. She has these water-skis, you see, and gosh, what a man wouldn't do for these water-skis! Could be, it's the water-skis I fell in love with, but one is never sure.

So here I am right on Waikiki Beach, skiing on the water with both my feet up in the air. I call this a stunt! It's very simple to water-ski, nothing to it. You don't even need to know how to swim. But it's better if you do. Waikiki Beach is my paradise. From morning to night I am out on my water-skis. And Gwendy bawls her head off on the shore. Guess she must be jealous.

Mum says Hawaii is frightfully touristy and far too many girls to make the place real interesting for her. Let's get out of here, she says, for heaven's sake. Twenty-five dollars a night without breakfast, Vat? Sheer robbery. And on top of it no night-life whatsoever. I watched Mum and Dad eat peanuts from a paper bag in our room. It was their dinner. How lucky can they be!

In the morning when Auntie Patsy comes with

Gwendy to go down to Waikiki Beach, Dad says, Nothing doing, I am going to change our tickets and get on the plane this afternoon. Another night here, and I am broke.

Sure, says Mum, looking at Auntie Patsy, This is the kind of honeymoon I always dreamt about. Peanuts in the bedroom and "No shopping, I beg you". To think, she says, that in Chicago we used to dream about Honolulu being an ideal place for a honeymoon. And Dad says from the door, What do you want a honeymoon for with these kids?—meaning Daisy and me, doubtless. And Mum starts packing our things together.

I am not interested in the Fiftieth State, which is what Auntie Patsy tells Mum, to cheer her up no doubt. What I do instead is go down to the lobby to get myself a few souvenirs. I tell Daisy to do a bit of modelling in her mu-mu, which is her newest outfit, *très chic, très Hawaii*, Mum says. It comes down to her ankles, like a kind of nightie, only it's made of stuff with flowers painted on it, which isn't even drip-dry, I know from Mum.

While Daisy parades up and down the lobby getting her photos taken, I help myself to 1 snorkel, 1 flipper, 1 crystal ball with a nude lady in it, 4 bars of Peanut Crunchies and That's All. When the lady comes back to the gift-shop, I hide them under my Hawaiian shirt and ask her for a copy of *Time Magazine*. Nobody who reads *Time Magazine* could be suspected of stealing, which is why I ask for that and not the *Newsweekly*. It gives her an idea of the kind of environment I am growing up in, and she smiles while she gives me the change.

The trouble is that when I go upstairs to pack my things away, Dad finds me with the crystal ball, and then hell breaks out. But not before he has a really good look at the lady whom you can see inside, which is typical of grown-ups. He returns the goods and makes me apologise, while Gwendy hangs six leis on my neck in exchange for the water-skis which I am not allowed to take with me because they belong to her.

And this is how we leave Honolulu. I am very sad as I look out of the window of the plane, because Waikiki Beach is the place I love. Perhaps some day I shall come back and spend a honeymoon all by myself there!

4 Meet the girls from Budapest

CAN you believe it, Dad asks us, as we get ready to get off the plane again, that here we are in America? I can't, but it doesn't matter. Because the first words I hear as we cross the tarmac are "Szervusz Oreg Haver!" which anybody can tell you is Hungarian for Hello.

The words come from a lady who Mum says is Auntie Yvonne, and they went to school together, I mean Mum and Auntie Yvonne, and isn't this true friendship, she asks, stepping into the Cadillac which stands right there under the sign of No Parking.

There is a nice crowd around the Cadillac, and while the policeman blows his whistle and yells, Get moving folks! Auntie Yvonne yells back to Dad, It's always the same, they never leave me alone, in Hollywood you have no privacy! She tries to start the Cadillac, while photographers are taking our pictures, but the car won't start on account of Auntie Yvonne not finding the key in her excitement.

Auntie Yvonne lives in Los Angeles, Calif., U.S.A. But when she finds the key at last, we drive to a place called Beverley Hills, and I am a bit confused. At the door there is Uncle Walter, who speaks German, and there is so much kissing and shouting that for a long time Daisy and I just stand around and nobody pays any notice to us.

At last Uncle Walter cries, Mein Gott, these poor kids must be starved, which is just at the moment when I want to jump into the swimming pool, having taken all of my clothes off beforehand. Auntie Yvonne had this swimming pool specially put in for us, she told Dad in the car. She bought it yesterday for these adorable darlings, which is Daisy and I, but no fear, we cannot have a swim, since breakfast is ready and we have to eat.

There is this big table spread out on the patio, and through the door rushes an old woman in black with an apron and a cap in white, and when she sees Mum she starts to cry and kisses her hand, calling her Miss Muki, naturally in Hungarian. Auntie Yvonne introduces her to us, she's Kati the cook from Budapest, who used to know Mum in the good old days, and there are special ischlers baked for the occasion and four cakes, better than the ones one could get at Gerbeaud's in the old country. And just in case Mum isn't homesick enough, there is a big dish of goulash too, and paté de foie gras, and chestnut purée, all for breakfast.

Well, we are going to stay with Auntie Yvonne for weeks, she has invited us and we cannot refuse, so I make the most of it. I eat a bit of everything, then I go upstairs and feel sick in Auntie Yvonne's pink bathroom. Afterwards, as I lie down on the bed to have a rest before my swim, Mum comes up to inform me that Auntie Yvonne's bed is genuine Louis Quinze. Louis Quinze, she says, was a French King once upon a time, and Quinze means Fifteen in French. It seems there were fifteen Kings all called Louis and people are apt to mix them up, especially people who are *nouveau riche*. Which is why Mum insists on giving me this bit of information.

However, Uncle Walter just comes into the bedroom —one never has privacy in Hollywood, really—and upon hearing Mum he tells me that everything in this place is phoney, beds, houses, and most of all the people. He is keen to open my eyes to the facts of life, which is why he switches on the TV which is in a cupboard that's pure baroque, so he says.

While I am lying down, I might as well tell you all about Auntie Yvonne and Los Angeles, Calif. Uncle Walter calls her *Schatzi*, which in German means Treasure. Auntie Yvonne is a real treasure to Uncle Walter, and her story is better than the movies.

Once upon a time, Auntie Yvonne went to school with Mum to a convent in Budapest. Then she became a war-bride together with her Mum, who was also a war-bride. They came to America, only to find that the men they were to marry weren't what they should have been. So they decided to stay poor rather than put up with them.

One day, Auntie Yvonne went to her cupboard and began to cry because she had nothing to wear. She said she wants to go back to Hungary and eat creamcakes in the little patisserie in the Vaci-utca. In Los Angeles, Calif., U.S.A. they couldn't make those creamcakes like in Hungary, besides she was poor and had nothing to wear. So what did her Mummy do but sit down and knit her a frock.

In this frock Auntie Yvonne went to Las Vegas to try her luck. However, in one day she had nothing left, and had to eat chocolates for dinner. She cried again, and as she did so, a good fairy came around and asked her, Where did you buy this beautiful frock? At Sak's? No, said Auntie Yvonne, my Mummy made it for me. Whereupon the good fairy offered her one hundred dollars if she sold her the frock, which Auntie Yvonne did, right on the spot. With the money, Auntie Yvonne hopped on a bus and went back to Los Angeles, Calif., where she said to her Mummy, Now get going and let's start knitting frocks, because we'll soon be rich.

And they knitted and knitted, night and day, nice frocks, some in silver, some in gold, some with mink around the neck. In no time Auntie Yvonne became so famous and rich that she married Uncle Walter who gave her a song as a wedding present.

Because Uncle Walter writes songs, and he is very, very famous. He gave me a song, and Daisy one, though I would have preferred that helicopter I saw in the drugstore. But Daisy was crazy about her song and started to dance immediately on top of the Bechstein Grand, while Uncle Walter played it for her on the piano.

This is when Auntie Yvonne got the idea. She watched Daisy dance, and yelled to Mum, That kid's a gold-mine! Wait till I give a cocktail party and introduce her to Hollywood. She then goes and rings up a man called Mischa who's a producer and asks him to come to her party to-morrow, because she has a surprise for him.

Meanwhile, I sneak out of the room and go for a splash in the pool.

5 *Mink for Daisy*

NEXT day there is this party. When we start to dress, it turns out that Daisy has nothing to wear. So Auntie Yvonne takes her off in the Cadillac, and they don't get back until most of the guests are there, and I have to entertain them with Uncle Walter and Martinis.

All Hollywood is there, when Auntie Yvonne and Daisy make their entrance. Everybody stops talking and some of the ladies faint, while Mischa comes forward, bows and says with his mouth full of caviar and accent: A star is born.

There is Daisy, covered from head to toe in a mink stole with a fluorescent ribbon in her hair. She is blowing kisses left, right and centre, just as Auntie Yvonne taught her to do. Somebody yells, Take it off, but Daisy is no fool. She won't take the mink off now that she achieved her ambition.

Dad whispers, Disgusting exhibition, and Zsa-Zsa hears it and has a fit, and somebody goes and rings up the fire brigade. There is this man in a bow-tie who begins to sing, "It was a marvellous party", whereupon Auntie Yvonne goes up to him and says, Noel, don't show off, just because you are English and want to make fun of us poor Hungarians.

You see, in Hollywood everybody is Hungarian, and that's all you need there, it's better than talent. The party is a great success, and Mischa promises a test for Daisy as soon as he can find a script to suit her. And after the guests are gone, Mum borrows Daisy's mink stole, and they go off to celebrate at the Beachcomber. while we eat up the leftovers and drink up everything that's left in the glasses.

Then Kati, the cook, takes us to a drive-in in her last year's Chev which she got for her birthday from Uncle Walter. It's a good show, not just cartoons and Wild Life in Alaska. There is some murder, and a lady who teaches Sunday school has an affair with a man who sings in a band, and when we get home we have this cream-cake made of almonds and rum. We eat it in the sitting-room, watching both the Late and the Horror Show.

I love Los Angeles, Calif., U.S.A.

6 *Why go to Los Angeles from Beverley Hills?*

ONE morning, while Mum has a bubble-bath and is talking about the good old days with Auntie Yvonne, I get an idea. I want to go to Disneyland which Kati says is right here in Los Angeles, Calif.

So I go downstairs to have a word with Uncle Walter. He is right there on the patio, doing his morning exercises. He wears a turban on his head and is wrapped in a bath-towel. As I come near him, he's poking his nose, which I know is necessary for Yoga. It helps deep-breathing.

He doesn't hear what I say, and Dad is busy having his breakfast on foie gras, which is why I decide to have a dip. However, there is a man cleaning the pool with a vacuum cleaner. He tells me that pools are sold in Los Angeles, Calif., U.S.A. complete with maintenance, which includes shampoo and set, and no water. So I can't have my swim.

At last Uncle Walter stops poking his nose, and I go and sit down beside him on the floor. I tell him that Mum and Auntie Yvonne are going shopping, besides you can't get any sense out of them once they talk about the good old days. We have been already a week in Los Angeles, Calif., U.S.A. and they still haven't covered the year they left school, let alone the happenings since.

I tell Uncle Walter that I want to go to Los Angeles, Calif., U.S.A., which sounds easier than Disneyland. I know once we get there, I shall find my way around and finish up in Disneyland, but it's no good rushing things with grown-ups.

When he hears me, Uncle Walter looks real puzzled.

Mein Kind, he says, Vat a verrückte idea! Vhy do you vant to go to Los Angeles? Nobody who is lucky to live in Beverley Hills ever goes there, unless summoned to court. He, Uncle Walter, who comes from a respectable *biedermeier* family in Grinzing, Austria, has never been to Los Angeles in his life.

And this gives him the clue to tell me a bit about his life-story. I sit it out, longing to be in Disneyland, while he tells me how he was discovered at the age of twenty and already a genius. He was very poor and was playing the piano in a café in Paris, when Metro-Goldwyn-Mayer spotted him and brought him out to Los Angeles, Calif., U.S.A. I pretend to feel sorry for him, since it's obvious that whoever brought him out had let him down sadly, since he told me earlier that he never saw Los Angeles, Calif., U.S.A.

There is nothing much you can do with grown-ups who do Yoga. I wait till Uncle Walter goes inside, and starts to play the piano. He plays it every morning, so Daisy can practise for her test. Then I just go and eat up what Dad's left from his breakfast. I am real hungry, because there is never any breakfast at Auntie Yvonne's. She and Mum eat nougats in the bubble-bath, while they talk about the good old days and their complexes. I am fed up listening to them, and here is just a little example of what I have to hear all day, while we live in this place.

It seems Mum and Auntie Yvonne have missed a lot in life. They could have had their luck, had it not been for Mater Schurcz and the convent and the black woollen socks they had to wear which gave them an over-developed conscience. As it is, Mum is spending the best years of her life in Australia, while Auntie Yvonne just sits and knits. Meanwhile, they eat nougats

all the time, and laugh so much that they roll down the swansdown bed.

Then Mum says to Auntie Yvonne, You sure gave back ten years of my life! whereupon Auntie Yvonne puts green eyeshadow on Mum and sprays her hair with gold and drapes the swansdown bedspread over her nightie. While she pours half a bottle of Arpège, Lanvin, on Mum's hand she says, Never mind, it's still not too late! Life starts at forty and you are only twenty-nine.

Now Mum jumps like she was bitten by a crocodile and shouts at Auntie Yvonne, with the result that they bring out each their passports which they compare carefully. Mum's passport says twenty-six and Auntie Yvonne's twenty-four. When Mum sees the difference, she shrugs her shoulders and says, It's your victory, I don't care. Personally, you were always the backward girl in our class.

So these are the sort of conversations I have to listen to, when what I really want is to go to Disneyland or have at least a swim in the pool which Auntie Yvonne claims she bought specially for us. But every day the man is maintaining the pool, one day shampoo, then set, and water only on Sundays, which is when people come to visit in Los Angeles, Calif. And as Uncle Walter says, nobody would visit you unless you had a pool. They have to maintain it all the week in order to make their guests happy.

I must say I agree with Dad that Hollywood is the last place for civilised people. I am of this opinion until the day comes when we go to Disneyland.

MD.

7 Disneyland—
here we come!

Disneyland is a lot of make-believe that's real. Herewith I have recorded my impressions of the place in drawing.

Dad was supposed to make colour-pictures; however, the silly man got so frightened from the crocodile which

25

c

opened his mouth right beside our boat that he dropped his camera into the Amazon River. Grown-ups are easy to scare. I could have told him the crocodile was make-believe. But they say one cannot teach one's parents anything.

I decided to become a Disneyland cowboy when I grow up. Then I can see the place free all day and every day.

Mum got this sunstroke and we had to hurry home to put her to bed. She can't take moon-rockets.

8 But she could do that in Europe!

AUNTIE YVONNE says we must stay here forever, or at least until Daisy has her movie test. Dad's getting anxious to broaden his mind and cash the cheque which he got from the Grant. Between them I am in a conflict. I begin to like the place.

Then one morning Kati gives notice. She says she wants to go back to Europe because she cannot take any more of this hectic Hollywood life. The real reason is that the dishwasher has broken down and the man took it away for repair and now Kati has to wash the dishes by hand. She could have done that if she stayed in Europe.

Well, Auntie Yvonne has a fit, and she says, Heavens, Kati, haven't you had this holiday in Europe only last year? In two years since you came to America you have been back once already. Which is pretty good going, since Kati doesn't even speak a word of English, but that doesn't stop her having airs and graces.

So to keep Kati happy, we all get into the Cadillac, except Dad, who disappeared early in the morning, and Uncle Walter, who still has to do his exercises. We drive to the Farmers' Market, where we can have lunch on paper plates and save Kati the washing up afterwards.

We eat a lot of ham sandwiches and cheese pancakes, and herrings until we burst. Kati gets into a better mood, and tells Auntie Yvonne that she changed her mind about the notice. Instead, she'll just fly off on a quick trip to Europe to see her sister once more, and will come back after a month.

Auntie Yvonne is thrilled, and we promptly go to shop for Kati's going-away outfit. She must impress her friends in Europe, after all, which is why we stop at a drugstore first, where we get her a pair of rubber gloves for washing up. While we are there, Auntie Yvonne buys me this underwater spear-gun, and the pram for Daisy, and a complete set of *Encyclopaedia Britannica* in paper-back edition for Dad to keep him happy in Los Angeles, Calif.

Then we go to Wiltshire Boul. and order a set of matching pigskin luggage for Kati, to be delivered after her initials are put on them in silver. You see, Auntie Yvonne has meanwhile got the idea that it won't be so bad to do the work by herself while Kati is in Europe, because we could move into the Bel Air hotel, all of us.

Naturally, we are included in the invitation, and Mum's in her element. As soon as the decision is made, she and Auntie Yvonne dash in to Sak's to choose a wardrobe, while we wait outside in the Cadillac. A few hours later they both stagger out with bags and parcels and a few loose frocks on their arms. And Auntie Yvonne gets into the car with a sigh and starts the motor, feeling real exhausted after such a busy day. Between them they tried on ninety-five frocks, so they could get a few to do them while we lived in the Bel Air.

We drive home to have an early night, and to our surprise find all our suitcases outside in the garden. With the luggage is Dad, looking impatient, and Uncle Walter, beaming all over his face.

What's the idea? asks Auntie Yvonne stepping out of the car.

Well, Dad tells her that all good things come to an end, besides he's fed up leading the life of an idle Hollywood parasite. Our plane is leaving for New York at eight, and we better make it snappy.

While I look up this word parasite in the *Encyclopaedia* which we bought for Dad, Uncle Walter informs his treasure that Mischa rang up and told him that Daisy's test was off. Mischa was so upset that he cried into the phone. However, it turned out that all Hollywood is the same, corrupt and based on the star system which is its downfall. It seems that as soon as they found a suitable script for Daisy, Zsa-Zsa got wind of it and decided to play the part herself. It is about a little girl who lived in Hungary. She liked all animals, especially minks and chinchillas because they have such a cuddly fur. Zsa-Zsa said that she could play the role to perfection, since Daisy speaks English without an accent. And this is how matters stand, which is why Mischa rang up to say how sorry he felt.

Well, hearing this, Mum gets real mad and she says, OK, I won't stay a minute longer in this swamp. I am taking my children to New York and give them real Kultur. Uncle Walter is all for culture, and he dances a jig right there on the lawn. And to show his pleasure even further, he announces that he will drive us to the airport HIMSELF.

Now this is a great moment in Uncle Walter's life. I mean not just that we are going, but the drive. You see, the airport is in Los Angeles, Calif., U.S.A. and at last he is going to make his acquaintance with this city. He can die a happy man or live even happier ever after.

9 *Where's America, please?*

I HAVE a horrible feeling that while we flew from Los Angeles, Calif., U.S.A. to New York, we have lost America.

I feel a bit let down. Don't know how to explain it to you. But there is Los Angeles, Calif., U.S.A. That isn't America. Then here we are in New York, which everybody tells us isn't America either. Very confusing.

New York is terrific. We live in this apartment and there are two lifts. I mean elevators. In New York they call lifts elevators. They don't speak proper English in New York.

What I love best is that here we have no garden. We can play instead in the street. This street is called Claremont Avenue, and is much better and more interesting than our garden at home. For instance, I could never ride my bike or roller-skate in our garden. I had to mind the plants. All I ever do in my garden is sit and moan and wish I was allowed to play in the street. Or visit somebody who lives in an apartment and has TV.

It's a lot of phooey, this business about gardens. If I want Nature or collect bugs and insects and acorns, or chase chipmunks, why, the best place is the park. Here in New York we have a park around the corner—Riverside Park. It has nice concrete paths and in the concrete there are these iron windows and through the holes in the windows we can watch the subway which goes underneath. I can't understand why people want Cadillacs all the time when a subway is much more fun. You can go everywhere on the subway and you don't have to park it. Go back and forth and change at Times Square, go by the express which is quick and the local which is slow. As long as you don't come up again, all the fun costs only a token.

I go to school in New York. My school is four blocks away and I cross over Broadway and go downstairs in a basement and then up with the elevator. There Sister Rosalia says, Good morning Paddy, my little Australian with the nice manners. I love Sister Rosalia because she never tells us to read or practise sums. She lets us draw and express ourselves. I am best when I can express myself. Every day I bring home my artwork which Mum calls pure primitive with an occasional touch of Chagall. I tell her it's crayon, not Chagall. But she won't understand. She collects my art in the kitchen drawer. One day, she says, she might arrange an exhibition of my works at Wildenstein's.

Daisy goes to Riverside Church from nine till twelve. Her school is on the fourteenth floor and all she does there all day is push a pram. The teacher, when Dad spoke to her about it, said, Don't worry, the kid has an inner compulsion which makes her want to push, push, push. I never tell Dad, but Daisy often tells me that she's awfully bored in her school. She is dying to go back to Hollywood and star in the movies with Uncle Walter. She has this crush on Uncle Walter, God knows why. I guess it's because he's a man. On the fourteenth floor at Riverside Church there are only ladies who teach kids how to push a pram.

Dad's at Columbia. He's awfully happy at last, because he can improve his mind without improving his Hungarian.

Only Mum's sad. Her friends are still away in Europe. You have no idea what autumn is like in New York. Mum says, this is the worst suburbia she has ever seen. All she sees is Riverside Park and the A & P on

Broadway. Never did she dream of life being so different in New York with kids and a family. She used to come to New York alone and unattached on holiday from college. This made all the difference to her Outlook.

I have an Aunt and an Uncle in New York. They are Hungarians but you can't notice it much until they talk to you. My Uncle is called Sanyi. Dad can't pronounce it so he calls him Alex. He called on us right after we arrived and asked Mum if she was OK for money. Mum told him about the Grant which was barely enough to keep us from starving. Oh, said Uncle Sanyi, looking real cheerful, You have a Grant from Mr. Carnegie! Now that's nice. You are very well off. With a bit of modesty you'll be able to manage. And on Sundays I shall take you all to the Bronx Zoo.

Mum said to Dad that Uncle Sanyi isn't typical of her family. He's an eccentric and she bets he has more money than the Queen, because all his life Uncle Sanyi never took a taxi but always goes by subway.

Mum claims she is Uncle Sanyi's favourite niece. She has this idea, because, when she came to New York years and years ago before she had Us and life could have been fun, only it wasn't, Uncle Sanyi had bought her a hamburger. But she can't remember quite well—it may even have been a cheeseburger. All she recalls is that Sanyi made her walk twice up and down the full length of Broadway and when she fainted, he bought her a hamburger (or a cheeseburger). Meanwhile, he lectured to her on What it Meant to be an Immigrant. Uncle Sanyi is an authority on Immigration. He came to New York almost thirty years ago.

Auntie Lilly is Sanyi's sister, which is why she is my aunt and also so very different from her brother. She is a doctor in a hospital in Union, New Jersey, which is just across the river.

Now there is one Hungarian, my Auntie Lilly, whom I like and don't feel ashamed of. She comes to see us between confinements. She is loaded with things, such as cream-cakes she brings for Mum but which she eats up herself on account of her diet.

Auntie Lilly is on a diet of boiled beef and spinach. This miserable food is barely enough to keep her soul alive. The rest she can squeeze into a size Sixteen at Bergdorf's. She feels awfully weak driving all that way from New Jersey to Claremont Avenue, which is why she stops halfway in Seventy-Second Street at a pastry-shop. She has to regain her strength there. They sell all sorts of cakes in this shop, mostly cream-cakes and chestnut-rolls and nougats. If you like those sort of things, you can get a cup of Viennese coffee served with an extra helping of whipped cream, to stop the dryness in your tummy.

But Auntie Lilly is in a hurry, so she just tells the lady, Please, pack up a dozen indianers (which are round chocolate cakes filled with cream inside), and one dozen dobos torte slices, and a few pounds of those tea biscuits, and two serves of chestnut purée with whipped cream. That'll be all to-day, thank you. I am only going as far as Hundred and Sixteenth and Clare-mont Avenue, to visit my darling nephew and niece.

Auntie Lilly promises to come to Europe with us next summer. She says she'll bring her car and maybe we can all go to Vienna together. She hasn't been to Vienna for five years, and she's dying to get her mouth full of real sacher torte which they make at Demmel's.

I am lucky to have relatives like Auntie Lilly and her brother, Sanyi.

10 *My friend Harry and the goldfish across the court*

WELL, here I am in New York, waiting for the boy who lives across the hall to come back from his summer holidays. Mum sits beside the phone, but no Hungarians ring up, because they are still in Europe.

I have one friend just now, and his name is Harry. He's the Liftman, or Elevator Man if you prefer it this way. Now and then I go downstairs and sit with him for a while. We sit on the green leather couch which stands in the lobby. It gives style to our building which otherwise isn't so hot, really. It has seen better days, Harry tells me.

When I am not in school, or in the park, or in the street, or in the lobby sitting on the green couch with Harry, I am at the window. Daisy and I can get lots of fun just standing by our window on the sixth floor. We look across a courtyard and watch the goings-on in other apartments. Such as that goldfish who swims in a bowl on the window-sill opposite.

That goldfish looks very sad and lonely, which is why I made this fishing tackle one day. I made it out of an old curtain-rod and a ball of string Harry gave me. I can't stand watching goldfish being sad and swimming round and round in circles. So I tie special flies on my fishing tackle, and practise fly-fishing for hours. I made these flies from toilet paper and they are as good as real. I have read in a magazine called *The Perfect Angler* or something that real sportsmen must use flies—never worms, baits, etc.

I let Daisy have my binoculars while I am fishing. She likes to watch this couple who are in love. They do a lot of kissing. Besides, they are brother and sister, but

Mum won't tell me that. I know the Bible, where it says, Love thy brethren. It doesn't say Love thy sister and kiss her all over the place. If there is a chapter like this in the Bible I must have missed it. Because I never kiss Daisy. It'd look as if I was wallowing in Sin, maybe.

There's also this old lady in the pink dressing gown, who stands all day in her window. She has a mirror in one hand and a pair of tweezers in the other. With the tweezers she plucks her chin which is kind of beardy. We watch her for a while, but it's always the same.

And, oh yes, there are these fire-escapes too, and a pram on the fifth floor landing. There is no baby in the pram, only a tree with purple leaves. Fancy having a tree grow out of an old pram.

What makes it so interesting standing there at our window is that one doesn't have to look at the sky. You just can't see the sky above the bricks, nor the sun. But I don't miss it, really, because for the moment I have got my heart set on that goldfish. I must catch it one of these days. Even if I have to use bait instead of my special flies made of toilet paper.

Our apartment belongs to a lady who is delayed in Guatemala where she had to supervise the assassination of the President. So until they find another President, we have this apartment on a lease. I mustn't paint on the walls, not even a mural of Our Lady above my bed where this patch is from a burst pipe.

There is wallpaper in the sitting-room which looks like my skin when I had the measles.

11 *Mum solves the Puerto-Rican problem*

M Y best friend in New York so far is Pedro Alvarez. He goes to the same school as me. When I met him for the first time, do you know he tried to show off. He said he has been to Australia which is near to the place he was born. His place is Puerto Rico.

Now I can't stand showing off, and I make this plain to Pedro Alvarez when we go out in the street for our lunch play-hour. We have the whole street to ourselves, I mean the kids who go to Corpus Christi. Not like in Melbourne, where one has to play cricket on the green, and go swimming every Wednesday, rain or shine.

Oh, I love New York ever so much! But about Pedro Alvarez, who is my friend. You see, I told him a few things when we were out in the street, and shrunk his nut, which means head. Kids in our school who show off have a swollen head. You must shrink it for them until it becomes normal size. When I get his head back into shape, I get up and tell him to shake hands on it. So we become friends. He also gives me a dollar, which we promptly take to the shop on the corner. We buy one artificial nose for me, one turtle, and an all-day sucker to share. He lets me keep the change which is a nickel.

Getting home from school I find Mum beside the phone, which as usual isn't ringing. The Hungarians are still abroad. So I suggest, How about we go and play with Pedro Alvarez who lives only a few blocks up from us. It's raining a little, and it's no fun for you to sit in the park while it rains, I say.

Well, she gets up and puts some lipstick on and says, Let's go. Daisy comes too, and on the way to Pedro

Alvarez's Mum explains that she has no objection to my friends, however she prefers to meet their parents socially. And with this she walks right in to the apartment where the Alvarez family lives.

Anyhow, the first thing we see is Pedro Alvarez's Mummy, who throws up her hands and says something which sounds like Jesus, Maria! Next, it turns out that she doesn't speak a word of English. Mum tries French, just in case, but Pedro Alvarez's Mummy only shakes the golden rings in her ears. She is very fat, and has on this pair of bright red matador pants over which she wears a green velvet skirt. It's clear the way she looks that she isn't Hungarian. No use trying.

However, they have this electric train right in the middle of the room, under the table. And Pedro Alvarez has more toys than I have seen anywhere else in the world. True, he has a few brothers and sisters, about one hundred, and they all sleep in the same bed. It's hard to understand.

Well, we play around for a while, until Mum feels tired of being an Esperanto dictionary, and she gets up and says, Sorry, we must be going. Anyhow, she explains to the golden ear-rings which shake and shake, This is only a First Visit, Madame, and I am afraid the fifteen minutes are up.

Well, Pedro Alvarez's Mummy isn't as formal as that, and she pushes Mum down on the chair and says, Momento, momento. Then Sacramento, but this she yells across the passage, when she sees that somebody else is in the kitchen taking a footbath. Nevertheless in no time at all she comes back with a huge tray, on it a lot of pink cakes and orangeade, and coffee for Mum who says it is the best she has ever had in New York.

While Mum sips her coffee, Daisy takes Juanita,

Pedro Alvarez's kid sister, and tells her to be dead and go lie down on the bed. She doesn't want to, whereupon Daisy herself lies on the bed, quite harmlessly really. There is an unholy scream from the bed, because it turns out that all the time while we are paying our First Visit at the Alvarez's Pedro's Dad is trying to get a wink of sleep on account of being out-of-work and tired.

As we leave Pedro Alvarez at five o'clock and walk home on Broadway, Mum explains me the Puerto-Rican Question. Briefly, she tells me she has no objection to my friends, regardless of race, colour and creed. (These are her words, quote.) I can go to play with Pedro Alvarez any time I want to, because Mum has no prejudices. However, she says, there is something basically wrong with this world. Here we are, four of us, each with his own bed, while Pedro Alvarez sleeps with his entire family in one bed.

The way to solve the Puerto-Rican problem would be simple, so Mum says, if only people were broad-minded enough either to give everybody a bed, or, even better, abolish beds altogether. Then we would become equals. We could all sleep on the floor. And to get to know each other really well, that is, to be able to have nice conversation with people who don't speak English, Mum has a colossal suggestion. Why don't the United Nations proclaim one universal language, the best and easiest language in the world . . . Hungarian!

12 *Look it up in the "New Yorker"*

I AM getting used to New York, especially since Jo-Jo, the boy across the hall, is back from his holidays. Jo-Jo and I have a lot in common. Such as, he likes TV too, but they don't have one either. Then his Dad is a Professor, which I can tell you is something we both feel ashamed of, but can't help. They took Jo-Jo to a doctor, he tells me, because he wouldn't eat frozen peas. He just wouldn't touch the stuff. He would eat hamburgers and hot-dogs, but not frozen peas. So this doctor had a look at him, and asked him a lot of questions. He was a nosey fellow, and at first Jo-Jo wouldn't answer him. Then he sent his Mum outside, and they got down to facts, man-to-man. When he found out that Jo-Jo's Dad was a Professor at Columbia, he shook his head sadly. This explains it, he said, then wrote something in a book. He told his Mum not to give him frozen peas any more, because Jo-Jo has an inferiority complex.

Sanyi took us to the Bronx Zoo on Sunday. It's the biggest Zoo in the world and really terrific. (As to my impressions, please see the drawing I did there on the spot. Lucky I took my sketchbook with me, because, as it happened, Sanyi didn't believe in colour-slides, which cost a lot of money, and offered me ten cents for each drawing I did.) Otherwise it's just like any other Zoo. Reminds me what Granny always says in Melbourne: there are all kinds of animals who make a world. She is right. Take for instance the giraffe. He wears these spotty pyjamas. (Spots are the rage at Sak's, Mum says.)

The penguins are real elegant. Just like my Dad, when he went once to dinner with the President. He put on all his decorations and couldn't do up the button

MD.

of his jacket on account of his stomach out in front.
Same as the penguins.

Even if it isn't Sunday and we can't go to the Bronx
Zoo, there's still a lot happening in New York. One
doesn't have to go to the park all the time. All we do is
get the *New Yorker* and look up what's happening.
Such as this Japanese No-drama, where we go Saturday.

It's special Japanese No-drama, recommended for kids. Mum takes us there, pays the twenty-five cents, then goes off to look at Auntie Daisy's baby who lives nearby.

I am crazy about Japanese No-drama. There is this Japanese man on the stage, and when the lights go off he moans. He sits on a blue cushion, wearing a black kimono, and he moans. A lot of the kids laugh, but that's because they don't understand. Japanese men are nervous when they have to dance for kids.

After a while this man stands up and stops moaning. He begins to wiggle his toes, while he screws up his eyes and waves a fan. He wears these gloves on his feet, you see, which make it easy to wiggle his big toes. Japanese, Mum says, have strange customs. They wear white gloves on their feet, among other things.

The amazing thing is that he can go on wiggling his toes, and fanning himself for two hours. Sometimes he puts a mask on. But I don't get scared. I understand No-drama, because I have a real Outlook.

Then there's always the museum. I like the Metropolitan best, although I go to see the stuffed animals in the other museum across the park, just to please the competition. But the Metropolitan is more fun, I can tell you. We go there whenever Mum has to make a quick trip to her outlet-store in the Bronx. No use dragging kids around when you try on frocks, she says, and parks us at the Metropolitan for the afternoon.

We have a dollar between us, which we take to the café downstairs. I would prefer the café upstairs; it is much nicer. But trust the management not to let kids in there on account of the nude statues which are decorating the pool.

After we spend our dollar on ice-creams, we come up

and go to the place where they have these Egyptian mummies. There is also this great pyramid which is ideal to play hide-and-seek in. And coffins by the hundred, some with mummies, some empty. One day Daisy lay down in an empty coffin and pretended to be a mummy. It was a great success on account of the lady with the dead-minks hanging around her neck, who brought her little boy to give him education at the Museum. She came over to Daisy and said to her boy, Look Cedric, this is a genuine Egyptian mummy, maybe even the Princess Nefertiti! It was then that Daisy decided to get another ice-cream downstairs, and got out of the coffin to the horror of the lady and her boy. His name was Cedric, very awful. They both screamed and we had to be removed.

We are often removed from the premises, which we don't mind at all. You see, what I omitted to say earlier is that you get your best education not inside the Museum but outside where they have this playground. So when we get removed, we just go outside and make our own fun.

This Metropolitan playground is full of nannies and poodles and kids in prams. There are very few adults (I mean mothers and fathers) because in this part of New York it's more chic to have nannies and poodles. You can tell those kids who play at this playground from a mile away. The playground has toys like this giraffe from F. A. O. Schwarz which cost 300 bucks and is really too big to play with, and makes the kid who tackles it frustrated. Besides, giraffes this size don't fit into prams, and are kind of awkward to carry.

Well, we sit down on a bench and have this game of our own. We pretend to be real poor. It's easy. All you need is a few holes in your socks and clothes, which you get anyhow inside the pyramids. You also have to remember not to wipe your nose. The rest is simple.

Somebody comes along and, seeing you, asks about your private life. So you give him the story. You tell him your Mummy is busy making money on the street. It's hard work which takes her all day. You mustn't speak about your Daddy except in strict confidence. He was taken away by the police years and years ago, and now he has to have a rest cure at Bellevue.

This isn't the only kind of story, of course, because stories come different and can be varied according to the gentleman or lady who's asking about your private life. The result is always the same. They give us money. Once Daisy and I collected twelve dollars between us just by telling a few people in the playground about our private lives.

With the nannies we have a different technique. We walk around their pram silently for an hour. Then we lean into it and cough right in the face of the kid who sits there. Or we just hang around scratching ourselves as if we had a nice disease. Nannies are frightened of diseases, especially coughs. They start flapping around you and try to shoo you away from the kid. So what you do is tell them that you cannot go away until your Mummy comes to fetch you, which won't be until dark. Mum never goes around New York in daylight, you say, because she has leprosy.

So ten to one we get at least a dollar for a taxi, so we can go far, far away. Which we do. We go to Auntie Daisy, who lives on Park Avenue, and watch TV.

13 *They live on Park Avenue for the climate*

Auntie Daisy is Mum's best friend, just like Auntie Yvonne. Only she is a DISAPPOINTMENT.

You see, what happened is this. She had this baby. She had him just as we came to New York. It was bad enough that she got married, but to have a baby just as we were coming was selfish and inconsiderate. (Quote Mum.) She should never have let Mum down like this . . . never. They went to the same convent together in Budapest.

Auntie Daisy lives on Park Avenue, which she owes not to herself but her family. She has a very big family, all living on Park Avenue on account of the climate. It's cooler there. I feel sorry for Auntie Daisy, because she would much rather live in Scarsdale than on Park Avenue, which is hell for her kid, anyhow. You got to get a nannie to take him for walks in the pram, which will give him a complex forever.

Rudi, the man Auntie Daisy married in Mum's absence and without consulting her, is not a Hungarian. He's worse. He's from Vienna. He doesn't like it on Park Avenue either, but has to put up with it for the time being. Rudi says that if they went back to Vienna he could live like a prince on half the dollars it costs in New York. He could have his own Schloss for shooting, and specially fattened trout for fishing. In New York he has to make do with under-sized trouts for which he fishes at a club in Long Island.

What with Auntie Daisy running after the nurse who runs after the baby, and Rudi taking the Olds every week-end to do his trout-fishing, and the rest of the Hungarians still away in Europe on account of the climate, Mum says the place isn't the same as it used to be.

So it happens that one Sunday, when Dad's away at Harvard, which is also a university, we have nowhere to go. Uncle Sanyi must move his mistress in the country, and we cannot go to the Bronx Zoo. Auntie Lilly has fifteen confinements and two Caesareans which is why she can't come over from New Jersey at the week-end. And Mum is very very sad.

Well, I want to cheer her up, which is why I sneak down to Harry, the Elevator Man, to ask his advice. I like old Harry very much, and when he sees me, he says, Hello Paddy, What can I do for you? I ask him if he knew of somebody who has a car and could take us for a drive in the country.

Gee, Paddy! Harry says, I am sorry, gee, but I leave my car at Jamaica every morning. He lives in Jamaica where he has four houses, three rented out and only one for the family. He also has a little farm in New England, not much really, but he asks me if we would like to come up and spend Thanksgiving with him and his wife, wouldn't it be fun? His wife, he says, would love to have us, she is used to Columbia people because his son is a Senator or something, and she could show us the real American way of life. We could have turkey and mince-pie and a bathroom for each of us.

This doesn't help me much because it isn't Thanksgiving yet. But I thank Harry, whom I like very much. I sit down for a while on the leather couch and listen to his problems, mainly taxation. It cripples him, it does. I don't understand much about taxation, mainly because Dad has only debts and they are tax-free, he says. But Harry is a rich man with property, which is why he can afford to be an Elevator Man and doesn't have to be a Professor.

What I like best about Harry is that he can fix anything for a dollar. True, his hands are a bit clumsy on account of this war injury, but he never charges more than a dollar when he messes up the tap or stops the motor in the frig or breaks the lamp in the hall. What he does is, he fixes it up afterwards, that is, he brings a handyman over from No. 22, whose name is Joe. He fixes everything that Harry messed up, and Mum claims he is in league with Harry to exploit the tenants.

I don't tell Harry that it looks as if we won't go to spend Thanksgiving with him, because it would break his heart. You see, Mum doesn't want to learn about the American way of life. This isn't why she came to New York. She wants to meet all the Hungarians who are at present in Europe. We must wait till they come back.

Mum says, New York isn't America, which I discovered already on the plane. But when Dad asked her to go to Harvard and have a look at the place, Mum said, No Thank You. No more Campus life for me, she says. I don't want to go near another Law School as long as I live, she says. I am superstitious, she says. You see, what happened was that Mum met Dad at a Law School in Chicago, and they got married there and she missed all her chances in life on account of that. Now all she can do is live happily ever after.

14 George the Count propositions my Mum

JUST as I am sitting there with Harry on the couch the buzzer goes and the door opens and in comes a man wearing black-and-white shoes and smoking a cigar. He also carries a big bunch of flowers. He comes straight over to us and says to Harry, Is it OK if I leave my car outside? I won't be long, couple of hours, maybe. It's only an imported MG and therefore hardly noticeable.

Harry wants to say something, when I poke him in the rib. You see, the man had just taken his glove off and is now searching around in his pocket, which I understand means a tip. Harry notices it too, and says, Sure, I'll do my best, and, lo and behold, the man slips him a Fiver, I swear.

The funny thing is that as we get into the elevator together, the man presses button Six. So just to be nice to him and give him a free ride, I press button Ten as soon as we reach the sixth floor. He doesn't appreciate my gesture, so I let him have his chance, and when he comes down to the sixth, I get out with him. I am interested where he is going.

Well, to my surprise, he presses our button. I am about to tell him that this is my apartment, and surely, he didn't come to visit me, when the door opens and there's Mum. She looks at the man, and throws her arms around his neck and they kiss. I find this kind of funny, to tell you the truth. So as the man wants to come inside, I just put my foot between him and the hallway and he trips over and falls face down on the floor. Mum can hardly rescue the flowers, which she grabs and takes to the kitchen, before the man can change his mind and tell her that they aren't meant for her.

I don't think the man is too happy when I sit down and look at him in the sitting-room. I don't think he understands kids from the way he looks back at me, which isn't flattering to anybody. And when Mum comes back, Daisy is with her, and there is a bit of introduction, just in case it isn't clear to the guest that we are the kids.

Mum is blushing real girlish, and rushes in and out, bringing coffee, and shouting in Hungarian. I forgot to mention that the man, of course, is Hungarian. His name is George, and he wears black-and-white shoes. Typical. Well, after a while he gets a bit tired of me staring at him, so he's obliged to take out his wallet and give me a dollar, which he says I should spend quickly. Right now, and down on Broadway. I thank him for the money and stay. This I owe to Dad, after all.

It transpires that this George is an old friend of Mum and he's just back from Europe. He invites Mum for a ride in his MG. Mum can be a good sport sometimes, because she jumps up and kisses George, and says, she won't be a minute and isn't it wonderful, just the very thing we wanted to do, only we haven't got a car. And the next minute she's back, dressed like last year's Christmas tree, and says, Let's go everybody!

Everybody? George asks in surprise. Sure, Mum says, The kids are dying to go for a bit of an outing, the poor things stuck in this awful flat all day. George says, Well, Muki, all I have is this tiny little MG for two, I wasn't quite prepared for this surprise or else I would have brought the Cady.

Never mind, Mum's in a good mood, and we all squeeze into the lift and ride downstairs, and say Hello to Harry, and go and inspect the MG outside. It's parked right on the footpath, looking very smart. Daisy and I love MGs, so we take our seats immediately.

George scratches his head and doesn't know what to do, whereupon Mum reminds him of the good old days in Budapest, when nine people could easily get into a Fiat Topolino, so what's wrong with an MG? But it looks like George has changed in America, because he can't quite see the fun of it. Which is why I suggest that Mum should take a taxi and follow us.

Well, George is resigned, and tells Mum where to go, and he gets in beside us and starts off in third. I absolutely love it. We roar through Broadway, the big park and down Fifth, with Mum in a taxi behind us. We all have fun, except George, who's kind of nervous as he chews his cigar.

We get to this restaurant, you see, which is right on the park, and Mum sails in, with us following. There's a very elegant gentleman in black, who bows so deep that I am afraid he may get stuck like an ostrich. But he is clever and when he gets up he says, Good morning, Count Barankowski! Good morning, Madame, nice to see you back in New York. I am sure I never saw him before, but Mum pretends she did.

Nothing I like more than a good lunch in a restaurant, which is why I order apple-pie à la mode, and hot-dogs. Mum likes to show off, and she starts talking French and the result is they bring this little traymobile around and we get a lot of hors d'oeuvre. It's nice and messy and a good way to start a meal.

George has no appetite, he says. He orders four Martinis, and the waiter puts them all in front of him. Mum has lobster after the hors d'oeuvre, and she is absolutely in her element. You can tell when Mum is in her element, which is usually when she can speak Hungarian, or show off in French in a restaurant.

They start talking about the good old days, and George asks, Do the kids understand Hungarian? Mum shakes her head quite innocently, because she doesn't know, of course, that Daisy and I understand every word. Naturally, we wouldn't dream of *speaking* it, we just pretend we don't know Hungarian, that's that. With Hungarians if you let them know you speak their language, they start straight off in another one. I am tired of learning a new language every day.

Mum says with her mouth full of lobster mornay, George, such a thrill to see you doing so well for yourself in a new country. Whereupon George downs his third Martini, and tells Mum that the Important Thing for every emigrant is to know his value and not to undersell himself. He has this wife Stella, you see, who is real crazy about him and even has his coat-of-arms embroidered all over her underwear. This Stella, George explains to Mum, is so rich that she can afford to keep a Hungarian in the style he's accustomed to. So this is why he has an MG for sports and a Cady for funerals and weddings.

I am listening with one ear to all this conversation, waiting, as I must, for the apple-pie. (The hot-dogs weren't half as good as what you get at the Automat!) Mum keeps eating solidly, because whenever Dad's away we never cook. You see, we are very easy to please, Daisy and I, and Mum likes to save up the household money so she can buy bargains at Bloomingdale's.

They are talking about money, which is, by the way, all that Hungarians care about. And George the Count asks Mum, How about your chances? Or, he says look·

ing at her thoughtfully, Are you just a devoted mother and housewife?

Mum scrapes the mushroom sauce off the silver plate, and says, What chances could I still have in life? George agrees with her, because he says, Mum made a fatal mistake years ago. As it is, emigrants have this choice: To marry or not to marry! Marry if they are men and not marry if they are ladies.

All in all the lunch wasn't such a terrific success. The apple-pie was dry and when I asked for a glass of liqueur George got up and called for the bill. He said, as we were walking through the lobby, the best Mum could do is put us into a boarding-house or some such institution, and take a second chance on her luck.

Which is why Mum felt insulted, because she isn't one of those girls. She has the true mother's instinct, besides her virtues.

George was in a hurry and forgot to offer us a lift home.

15 *I hate antiques (especially my brass bed)*

I KNOW something's bothering Mum and it isn't Hallowe'en.

Why? This afternoon when we went into Reubens to share a Pompadour sandwich between us, she took the smallest piece and left most of it on her plate. It isn't like Mum, I can tell you.

Every second afternoon we go to the Waldorf to see if there's any mail for Mum. You see, Mum has an old friend from Hungary who works in the kitchen at the Waldorf and his friend is in the office there, which is why Mum made this arrangement to have our letters sent to the Waldorf-Astoria. It's good for the prestige, she says, and you got to have prestige if you want to succeed in this world. Just imagine how people would treat you if they knew that you lived in Claremont Avenue on a Grant!

Going to the Waldorf for our mail takes a whole afternoon. We get on the bus on Riverside and get off at the Plaza. We walk down Fifth and spend some time looking at the shops. I love Cartier's best, because there they have the cutest ideas in the windows. Like this little carriage made with rubies and diamonds which stands in the middle of a street, which Mum says is a picture straight out of "vieille Paris". I think it's cute. They even have these olden-days street-lamps done from rubies and diamonds, with poodles to match their sparkle. It's all fake, of course, I mean make-believe, though Mum says the rocks are genuine. Daisy wants one of the poodles very badly, and she asks the gentleman who is behind us, Would you get me that poodle, please? The gentleman looks at Mum kind of curiously, but doesn't get the chance to make a pass at her. You see, Mum hates strangers making a pass at her, she finds it humiliating. So she just takes Daisy by the hand and says, Let's go, children!

What I hate is Madison Avenue. Mum always takes us home that way so she can look at the antique shops. She gets kind of dreamy once she sees an antique shop, and won't move for hours. It wouldn't be so bad if there was only one antique shop in the whole avenue. But what happens is we walk these forty blocks, which is quite a lot, stopping in front of every window, hundreds of them, one after the other.

Mum's crazy about antiques which is why our house in Melbourne looks such a mess. She calls it Mixed Period, but I can tell you it's only junk. I have to sleep in a brass bed, on account of the colour scheme. It makes the most awful noise in the world. And we have a chair which Dad says must have been a prop in *Aida*, whatever that is. Mum claims it's the Emir's throne from Morocco. The fact is, it's got this back which looks like a gong, when you sit in it you get the sensation as if you sat on a gong, if you know what I mean.

We also have the whole panelling of a baroque church in our sitting-room, which Mum picked up at an auction for a song. I have no idea how much she paid for it, but it must have been the earth. All it's good for is for Dad to keep his French cognac inside it. You see, Dad's a connoisseur. He drinks French cognac himself and gives his guests Australian brandy. They don't know the difference, especially as he serves the Australian brandy in a French bottle and vice versa, which is Latin, meaning that he pours the cognac into a bottle labelled Australian brandy.

So this is the reason why I don't like Madison Avenue.

16 *How to be a best-seller in Japanese*

Now I know what's upsetting Mum. She hasn't made her first million yet, and she isn't even famous. I learned this last night when I was listening in on the conversation Mum had with Harry over a dish called nasi-goreng.

This Harry isn't Harry the Liftman, just in case you get confused. He's a writer. He came to Melbourne some time ago, when we had the Olympic Games. He came on a scooter all the way from America. To make it more complicated, he rode his Vespa first to Europe, because it's kind of simple to come to Melbourne direct from America. It's been done before, and Harry likes things that are a novelty. Also, he says, they sell better. I mean, stories which he writes when he does something nobody ever did before, like riding a scooter to Melbourne, Australia, through Europe.

Mum asked Harry to dinner in desperation. She made this nasi-goreng, which is her specialty. She picked up the recipe in Java, wherever that is. It's bound to impress everybody, except people who lived in Java. We had hot-dogs and were sent to bed.

Well, Harry said to Mum, It's time you do something about your books. Mum said, Why, I have just received the last shipment back from the seventh publisher this afternoon. (This explains the heavy parcel we picked up at the Waldorf.) But Harry said, You go the wrong way about it, let me tell you. He did.

The result was that next morning we had a bath. I am always suspicious when we have to have a bath in the morning. It was school holiday, I forgot to mention. Then Mum got all her books together, six novels and two cooking books. And we got on the subway and got off at Forty-Second Street. We turned left on Forty-Second Street and walked a few blocks and then we met Mr. Jackinson.

Mr. Jackinson has an office on the sixth floor in Forty-Second Street. He is a literary agent. Well, we go in and shake hands, and make an impression. I am wearing my new cowboy jacket I got from Auntie Lilly. Mum wears Daisy's mink stole, and Daisy my overcoat from last year. She howls. Dad's at Yale, which is why we had to have this bath and come along.

Mr. Jackinson is a nice man and he doesn't make a pass at Mum. Instead, he looks kind of interested and says, May I see the manuscripts? But before Mum shows them to him, she briefly tells what she calls the synopsis. The word is new to me, but not the stories.

You see, I know Mum's stories by heart. They are really quite simple. She tells them again to Mr. Jackinson, and occasionally I correct her. This makes Mr. Jackinson laugh while he keeps typing on his typewriter. He can listen to stories while he types to his clients. He is used to authors, because that's his business.

Well, Mum says, I have these six novels, which are really a saga. They are about a little girl who had to leave Hungary on account of the Russians. Ah, says Mr. Jackinson, addressing an envelope, Autobiography? Not at all, says Mum modestly, Although you may perceive a certain similarity between the events in the books and my life. But I call the girl Arabella. She escapes from the naughty Russians and goes across the border. It's night-time and moonlight, and very dangerous. Everywhere dogs are barking. There are mines exploding and people get killed, but not Arabella. All she meets is these two Russians, who are drunk. They almost rape her, but in the last minute she gets this wonderful idea, and gives them this genuine holy ikon which is a family heirloom. When the Russians see the black face of the Madonna by moonlight, they cross themselves and fall to their knees. Whereupon Arabella is miraculously saved.

Now, Mr. Jackinson says, What about the other books? Mum looks a bit surprised and starts off on Chapter Two, but she doesn't get far, because Mr. Jackinson begins to shake his head sadly and says, The market is full of escape stories, and they are kind of dated. What I am looking for is something different. Such as a lot of sex and a bit of science fiction. Perhaps, if Mum could write a book about the Chinese invasion which will take place in 1984—well, that could be made into a hit. She could use Arabella as a protagonist, no need to discard her. All she has to do is rewrite her stories and place them in Australia, somewhere on the beach, where this Chinese invasion is happening. Arabella is fleeing the Chinese, and she gets into this atomic submarine and before she knows where she is, she is in Antarctica. That's the land of Futurama, says Mr. Jackinson. From there on, the story is really simple to write. What Mum must observe is to keep the public interested. Like putting in a bit of sex between Arabella and this Antarctic explorer who is in a wheel-chair because his legs had to be amputated on account of frostbite.

I listen interestedly, while Mum shakes her head. As a last resort she puts her two cookery books on the desk. Ah, Mr. Jackinson's eyes light up, now here's something that has possibilities. He flips through the pages, and smiles. Very good, he says, excellent. I like this Japanese pastrami sandwich best, he says, and licks his

E

lips. And these Indian blintzas—absolutely mouth-watering!

Mum is about to smile, when Mr. Jackinson hands the books back to her. He says they have definite possibilities. The market at present is in need of authentic Japanese and Chinese recipes. Now what Mum must do is to take these manuscripts home, brush them up, prepare them in a shape that would appeal to a publisher and . . . rewrite them in Chinese and Japanese. The public, Mr. Jackinson says, is no longer interested in *Good Housekeeping* recipes. Thanks to *Gourmet* magazine, they are connoisseurs with discriminating palates. If Mum wants these books to sell, she's got to make them different. Recipes in Chinese and Japanese! With Hokusai prints and Fujita drawings to fill in the gaps! He gets up and shakes hands with us, and assures Mum that she is definitely on the right track. As soon as she delivers the first chapter, he's going to get her an advance on the royalties.

On our way home, we stop by a bookshop and get these four dictionaries for twenty-five dollars, one Malay, one Japanese, one Chinese and one in Urdu (which, the man tells us, is the most popular Indian dialect).

Then we go the roundabout way, which is by Mrs. Herbst's cake-shop on Third, where Auntie Daisy is waiting to hear the news about Mum's luck as a best-seller.

17 *Hungarian music with my wiener schnitzel*

WE have two helpings of everything, that is marron purée, and apfelstrudel and dobos torte, because the occasion calls for celebration. Auntie Daisy pays the bill and Mr. Herbst, who is the husband of the Strudel Queen, comes out from the kitchen and congratulates us. Mum is very excited, especially when she thinks of the unlimited prospects which Mr. Jackinson hinted at. She tells Auntie Daisy and Mr. Herbst and the whole cake-shop in Hungarian that her book will be made into a movie, all she needs to do is change the title from *Oriental Recipes* to something more catchy. Auntie Daisy has a few suggestions, and they agree that *Love in an Opium Den* would be the best title of the year. And parts of it could be sold to *Post* in serial form, again under a different title, such as *I was Mao's Concubine* or *How I changed from Communism to Buddhism*.

When you have afternoon tea at Mrs. Herbst's shop, you sure work up an appetite. Well, no sooner did we finish our indianer, which Auntie Daisy orders "pour la bonne bouche" (that's French, meaning "to take the taste of the dobos torte away"), than Mum gets a colossal idea.

It turns out that both she and Auntie Daisy are grass widows, what with Dad being away at Yale and Rudi shooting buffaloes in the Wild West with a visiting Archduke, and the Oldsmobile at the door to take us on a gastronomic bender around New York. There is a bit of argument about us, but in the end Mum wins, and she says, No harm if the kids get a broad Outlook, they've never been around the town in style, which is why all four of us get into the car and drive a few blocks down to a movie.

It's a good film, and just right to get us into a mood for goulash. The story is about a Hungarian gentleman and a Hungarian lady who fall in love. They do a lot of singing and dancing with gypsies playing to them until they drop dead (the gypsies—not the gentleman and the lady).

Well, there's a bit of excitement when it turns out that the lady is really a Countess, and the gentleman is not a gentleman but an F.B.I. agent. You should have heard the audience! But nobody shrieked louder than Mum with Auntie Daisy playing second bass to her, which is why I don't know how the film ended, because the management came with electric torches and asked us to Please Leave the Premises.

Anyhow, it was night-time by then, and what we do is, we get into the Olds and drive a couple of blocks and go to the Hungarian restaurant to have our dinner. I am good and hungry and so is Daisy, and while we study the menu, who should come in but George the Count and two of his friends. They are incognito, which is why they wear those Tyrolean hats and dark glasses, because their wives don't know where they are; they think they are at a board-meeting.

I try not to be disturbed by the company, and order wiener schnitzel for myself and chicken paprika for Daisy, only legs please. And I ask for Barbara Ann potato chips, which I saw on TV, but trust these Hungarians, they don't know what they are, and the waiter brings home-made chips instead, which aren't as good, but never mind.

While we eat, the headwaiter, who naturally recognises George the Count and his friends, even though they are incognito, sends across the street for the gypsies. You see, it doesn't pay for the restaurant to have gypsies all the time on the premises, since most Hungarians eat only the menu of the day which is Two dollars and Fifty cents, and no gypsy music included. But for high-class customers, such as us, the gypsies come over from where they have their cave across the street, where you can have your fortune told for a Dollar and a lot of other things too, but those are not for children.

Well, I must say we enjoy ourselves, what with Daisy doing her dance on the table, and me yelling my head off, while the *primas* (the man with the moustache who leads the band) plays his music right into Mum's ear. Frankly, it's a lot of *Schmalz*, but you can't help it when you have this wild Hungarian blood in your veins, like I do, it just demonstrates itself. A person cannot suppress his ancestry, which is why I like my wiener schnitzel with gypsy music.

It's almost midnight when we get out of the place, but not before letting the gypsies kiss our hands and call me Prince and Daisy Princess. (Gypsies have this little trick whereby everybody is one better than he really is, and to tell you the truth, I didn't object.) Next we get into the Olds, all seven of us and drive to Times Square to see the man blow smoke-rings through his mouth.

Well, no evening is an evening in New York unless you drive in a fiacre in Central Park. So we just leave the Olds somewhere under a tree, and hop into a fiacre, all seven of us, with me sitting up beside the coachman, naturally. And there is this moon, which is big and real, or maybe it's Sputnik, but who cares! After a glass or two of tokay, even Sputnik looks like the moon, when you have the Hungarian capacity for looking at nature through rosy eyes.

And before we know where we are, the fiacre takes us to a night-club, and there, as we get out, George the Count wraps his coat around us and smuggles us inside. George the Count can be a good sport, especially when he's drunk. You see, they got this thing against children in night-clubs, and he doesn't like to spoil our fun, which is why he puts his coat under the table, kind of odd but eccentric. And we crawl out and provided we don't get our heads above the table, we can observe the goings-on, which are plenty. True, we mostly see what goes on under the table, but that's good too.

And to this fun add Gyuri Feyer playing the piano! He plays all Mum's and Auntie Daisy's favourites, which he remembers they liked in the good old days in Budapest, such as "Vaci-utcan, Vaci-utcan", which is a typical Hungarian folk song and an Echo from old Budapest.

Which comes to show that a person can have a lot of exciting things happen to him in New York at night-time. This is one of the reasons why I simply adore the place!

18 *Naturally it never snows in Melbourne*

WELL, we had Thanksgiving, but we didn't have our turkey. Only chicken à la kiev and cherry strudel from Mrs. Herbst's. You see, Dad said we were just about down to our last nickel, and no hope of getting more out of Mr. Carnegie, on account of him being dead and R.I.P. (which is Latin, meant for tombstones, Dad says).

The trouble with New York is that Christmas there comes right after Thanksgiving. I mean, no sooner did you swallow your chicken kiev than Harry brings you the mistletoe to put on your door—gratis and free of good will. And the streets are all decorated with reindeers and jingle-bells, and you can't help being worried about money.

Mum isn't making much progress with her Japanese. She works every morning, and all she learned from the dictionary was that the Japanese have a queer way of writing down plain things, such as, Take a finely chopped onion and sauté until you hear it sizzling in the pan. It just can't be put in Japanese, this sizzling sound. Mum is depressed.

I forgot to say that yesterday I saw snow for the first time in six years, that is, my life. Real snow, I mean, and not just the stuff you spray on your Christmas tree in Melbourne, Australia, where Christmas comes in summer-time and Santa wears bathers under his cloak. (I saw it with my own eyes, last year, when he arrived in front of a department store in Melbourne, Australia. Striped bathers, black-and-white!)

To see the snow better we went to Bear Mountain Park. At the block where we play, next to Barnard, it melted very quickly. So Uncle Sanyi drove us to Bear

Mountain Park and boy, did I go wild there! I love the taste of snow, and to roll in it, and throw snowballs at people, it's just beaut. I only wish Melbourne didn't have everything upside-down, and we could have snow there at Christmas-time. There's nothing like a white Christmas.

In Melbourne it never snows. It just rains, and gets colder and colder, until it's so cold that you have to go to bed wearing mittens and socks on your feet. You see, it's especially cold inside the house and in your own bed in Melbourne, Australia, where the sun always shines, except for eight months, when it's winter. Because the pioneers swallowed this tripe about sunny Australia, people don't have central heating in their houses. The say it's not cricket and definitely un-English. It's much better and more pioneer to freeze, because our forefathers did the same, and they built Australia with their own hands.

Mum says her forefathers weren't pioneers but good *biedermeier* citizens in Central Europe, where every room had a stove going, and not just one fireplace in the sitting-room, which isn't lit on account of the cricket, like in Australia.

Anyhow, I have no prejudices, but I can say, I love the snow and the central heating. And I love my new waterproof ski-pants which, by the way, are the cause of all the trouble.

You see, we had to have nice snow-clothes, and although Dad wanted to wait until Christmas proper when aunties and uncles would have given them to us under the tree, Mum said, Pat, the temperature is twelve below and you want these children to die from the cold? Without waiting for the answer, we went to Bloomingdale's to outfit ourselves. And on our way home Mum made this discovery that we haven't got money even for an espresso. We usually drop in at the espresso in Fifty-Sixth, no matter where we happen to be. You can get there easy by taxi, even from the Bronx. We have no money, and Christmas is right around the corner, where the lady with the bunions sells the trees already. Well, it's such a sad business, that what we must do is get an idea, and get it real quick.

When Mum wants an idea in New York, U.S.A., she goes to Auntie Daisy's old Dad, whose name is Uncle Feri. Uncle Feri lives near Auntie Daisy, on Park Avenue. He would be a millionaire, except for his relatives who all sponge on him, or, to say the least, live on his wit's end. You can't be a millionaire with forty-four relatives all sponging on you, not even Uncle Feri can, what with the difficulties of a new language on top of it.

In Hungary Uncle Feri was a millionaire, and he has such a good brain that he has no hair left on his head, which is bald. When he thinks about an idea, he likes to push his glasses on top of his head, and scratch his pants a bit until he hits on it. I feel sorry for Uncle Feri, on account of all the people coming to get an idea from him. They stay until he gives them money. Hungarians cost Uncle Feri a fortune.

But Mum wanted no money, only a genuine idea: How to get rich quickly, before Christmas. She says to Uncle Feri, who switches the TV on specially for Daisy and I, because he likes kids who aren't his relatives, Mum says, Uncle Feri, they tell me money is lying on the street in America. So what can I do to get a few hundred, let's say a maximum of a thousand to tide us over until we go to Europe?

Wait a moment, says Uncle Feri as he goes to the door, where one of the relatives has just appeared, wanting his cheque. Uncle Feri gives him the cheque, because it pays him to pay his relatives not to come inside and try to be helpful to him in business matters. He gives cheques to most of his relatives to stay away. They can be deducted from his income tax.

Mum waits patiently, because she has great respect for Uncle Feri. But when he comes back, I am just adjusting my little chair so I can see Popeye better on the screen, and sure enough, Uncle Feri trips over this chair and would fall on the rug, if I didn't catch him quick. This incident is what gives him the idea.

He looks at me thoughtfully, then to see me better, pushes his glasses down on his nose. I got it! he cries at last and puts his arms over me. Well, he cries, the Big Idea is right here under my nose! It's the boy. It's Patrick!

Now it's Mum's turn to look surprised, but not for long. It turns out that Uncle Feri's Big Idea concerns me, Paddy. He puts the proposition to Mum, whereby he says I must go on TV.

You have a real gold-mine in the boy, says Uncle Feri, while I make my best Popeye face to justify his faith in me. He'll go on a Quiz Show! he says. He'll be a hit! He'll make money, you won't be able to stop him. All we need is, says Uncle Feri, to make him specialise in one field which is yet untapped.

Mum says, How about Cooking? Uncle Feri says, No, that was done by a sailor. Mum says Atom physics. Uncle Feri says, No, he's too old for that. Mum says, Well, I'll be darned (or something that sounds like that but means something quite different in Hungarian), whereupon Uncle Feri hits a nail on his head.

We'll let him specialise in Sex! And with these words he runs to the library and comes back with a heap of books which make him stagger under their weight. I lose interest in the idea pretty quickly, but not Mum. She and Uncle Feri and Auntie Daisy, who has just arrived with the baby, on account of the nurse's day off, get into a state of excitement. They talk and shout and look at the books, and the result is that I am going on a Quiz Show next Thursday.

19 *In vain I learn all about the Marquis de Sade*

THE days that follow are a nightmare. As soon as I come home from school, Mum takes a book and we go down to Riverside Park and sit on a quiet bench. She starts with words first, which I have to repeat after her. I can tell you a lot about babies, and how they are made, but frankly, that has nothing to do with Sex. The words I repeat until I am blue in the face are real tongue-twisters. Like Masochism. Or Oedipus Complex. Or Pederast. I ask what Pederast means, but she says, Don't worry, you wouldn't understand it anyhow. Well, I ask you, what's the good of being an expert when you don't even understand what you are talking about.

I gave Harry the Liftman a fright when I greeted him with a nice, cheery Pederast! He wasn't sure whether I was complimenting him on the occasion of his silver wedding, which he told us took place quietly in Greenwich, Conn.

But it's not only words I have to learn, oh no! For instance, Mum opens this book, and says: The Marquis de Sade? I answer: Born 1740 and dead in 1814. Then Mum says: Who invented Sex? First, I thought the answer was the Hungarians. Everything else in the world is invented by Hungarians. But Mum says, No, Paddy. Hungarians did not invent Sex, they only like to talk about it. It was Sigmund Freud who invented Sex. So I say automatically Born in Freiberg, 1856.

There is no limit to my knowledge. I am a fountain. I go to bed with sex on my mind and wake up with sex. If I hadn't set my heart on that electric train I saw at Lionel's with Jo-Jo, I wouldn't be here any more. And to think that there are people who believe that in America money is lying in the street, all you have to do is bend down and pick it up.

Just another stupid piece of Russian propaganda!

Well, Thursday morning, naturally, I must have a bath. Then Mum chooses the outfit I shall wear, such as this blue corduroy jacket I got from Auntie Daisy, a white shirt with a stiff collar and Dad's Magdalen tie. (He went to Magdalen College, Oxford, and has never been the same since.) To my surprise we take a taxi, the fare of which Mum advances on the strength of my winnings. She thinks I haven't seen her break my piggy-bank while we had our cornflakes! She writes down the expense in a little book, which says PADDY'S EXPENSE ACCOUNT.

I am important. I have arrived. Daisy is in bed at home with the German measles and Daddy. I mean Dad is in bed and Daisy crawled in beside him, so he shouldn't feel lonely.

We get out in Madison Avenue, and I have this moment of horror, thinking—we are going in to buy the antique chamber pot which Mum had her eyes on since September. She may even put the cost down under my expenses.

The antique shop is in the same building, but we don't stop by the window. We go inside the lobby and zoom up to the tenth floor, and there take a turn to the left, where it says Stairs. We climb the stairs to a penthouse, where we open the door and say to a lady who's putting Taj Mahal Gold on her finger-nails, Excuse me Miss, we have this appointment for eleven o'clock to see Mr. Smith.

She blows on her finger-nails while with the brush points at the door which says No Entrance. We enter, nevertheless.

Inside, beside a desk, a gentleman is eating a pastrami-on-rye. Apparently it doesn't bother him that there are about a hundred people in the room with him, all sitting at little desks like we used to have in my school in Melbourne, writing furiously on pieces of paper.

Mum flashes her best smile at Mr. Smith, who, just in case he forgets his name when he has to sign it on a cheque, has it written down in silver letters on a piece of wood on his desk. Before Mum can introduce me to Mr. Smith, he pushes two large pieces of paper in front of her, then another smaller piece of paper, and says, Sign here! He speaks with his mouth full, which is bad form.

Mum says, Excuse me, but I am afraid there is some mistake. I brought my little boy to take part in the show to-night. It's all arranged. Then she turns to me and says, Greet Mr. Smith nicely, Paddy. I do, but I don't feel like it. He takes a luscious bite from his sandwich and taps one greasy finger on the smaller piece of paper. Sign here; he repeats.

Mum signs. What else can she do? Then she looks at Mr. Smith and tries another of her famous smiles, the one with the corners of her mouth twisted upwards. No effect. Mr. Smith must be tired of us, because he slams the rest of his sandwich on the table, and says to Mum, Take Desk 15, and fill out the forms. The boy must wait outside.

Mum gives me a wink, and sadly I withdraw from the scene. Outside, the young lady has finished putting

Taj Mahal Gold on her last finger. She sees me and asks, Would I mind keeping the desk for her, she won't be a minute, she'll just run downstairs to have her hair set. I say OK and take my seat behind the desk.

I experiment with the Taj Mahal Gold, first on the wall, then on Dad's Magdalen tie. It has these white lilies embroidered on black, and I feel they can be improved. Which is why I set myself to the task and paint them gold.

I am pretty absorbed when suddenly someone behind my back begins to screech: Sonny boy! Cockadoodoo-looo! I look back, and there's a parrot sitting on the shoulder of an old lady, staring at me real cheeky. I say, I beg your pardon, whereupon the lady inquires about Mr. Smith. She shows me a letter, which I don't bother to read because it's in small print anyhow, and I am only familiar with capital letters, and says, she's been asked to present herself to be quizzed at eleven a.m. Her subject is the History of Anarchy in Babylon.

It costs me nothing, so I just send her inside, together with the bird, who by the way left his visit card right there on my tie. I apply Translucent Nailvarnish Remover, which takes most of it off. Some people have strange ideas about pets. For instance, it would never occur to me to go to Madison Avenue with Myrtle, our turtle. It just isn't done. Even though Myrtle is completely house-trained, and would never misbehave herself anywhere.

Well, I am painting this last lily gold when the door opens and out comes Mum. I can see at once that there is something wrong. However, she stays dumb all the way down to the lobby, and when I suggest we go to

Schraft's for our morning ice-cream, she follows me meekly.

Only at Schraft's when I order her a double banana split (it comes out of my expense account, so I can afford to be generous), does she finally tell me what happens. Well, she had these questions to answer, one hundred of them. She had to make noughts and crosses after each question, which sounds easy. The truth is, that though she put noughts and crosses all over the two pages, there was only one question she could answer and even that she wasn't quite sure about. It had something to do with Napoleon and Austerlitz. She thinks he won the battle.

Well, once Mum begins to talk you can't stop her. And on top of it she was so furious that she kept shouting about Babe Ruth and who the hell thinks a cultured European of noble descent would know the answer for questions like, "Who was the Captain of the Brooklyn Dodgers in 1928?" What do they take me for, Mum shouts, a football coach? Me, with my European background and three years at the University of Budapest.

It seems, you see, that they give people this test before giving them a chance to express their wishes and personality in front of the camera. It's all a damn' cheat, Mum says, in her best Oxford English. Why, years ago the reason she flunked out of Law School at Chicago was because of such a test. The Prof never gave her a chance to demonstrate her knowledge in Constitutional Law in more congenial surroundings, and by word of mouth and not on paper, besides.

I feel real sad for Mum, because, after all, she had to go through this ordeal on account of her family. What's more, she unselfishly arranged for the test on my behalf. Mum knew that she had no chances of getting on the Quiz Show herself. She knows nothing about Sex. She went to that convent in Budapest, where Mater Schurcz told them that Sex was a dirty word.

The result is that we didn't make our 64,000 dollars on TV. Guess we are just a bit unlucky.

20 *Imperial Peking Dinner for Christmas*

THERE is no other memory quite comparable to the first Christmas when you are allowed to buy your own Christmas tree. It's the day when you become an equal to your Mum and Dad.

Dad takes us down to Broadway on the morning of the twenty-fourth. We wait that long, because sure enough the tree which only yesterday was marked for 5 dollars is a dollar now. We buy it from the old lady who complains to customers that her bunion is killing her. Mum says she should soak it in a brandy bath, guaranteed relief. The lady is so pleased with this recipe that she lets us have the tree for 80 cents.

Mum doesn't believe in spending good dollars on decorations, which is why Miss Ford comes around, and in the name of herself and Mr. Carnegie presents us with the necessities. She brings enough to make the tree in front of the Rockefeller Plaza look overdressed and lets me spray the snow on, which I can do real well.

Daisy is still a little kid and Miss Ford is pretty worried that her illusions will suffer if she discovers that trees are bought and not brought by Father Christmas. So I just tell the kid that this year we are in New York City, which is so big that Father Christmas cannot bring everybody a tree himself, on account of the parking space problems and the housing space question, let alone the overcrowding due to the Puerto-Rican influx. I must say the kid takes it well, she couldn't care less who brings the Christmas tree as long as she gets what she wanted for a long time from F.A.O. Schwarz's boutique. What she wanted is this travelling wardrobe for her doll, complete with mink coat. Boy, she'll be disillusioned, I can tell already.

I have looked at the parcels in secret, which keep arriving for days now. Terrific stuff. Do you know that even the Hungarian League for the Restitution of the Monarchy has sent us toys? They sent me this Hungarian hussar on a horse, carved out of wood. Kind of primitive, but a nice touch.

We have this party on Christmas Eve, in accordance with Mum's traditions. You see, in Hungary Santa doesn't put his gifts into stockings which are hung on the mantelpiece. What they had instead, in the good old days, was a big dinner party, and afterwards the tree got lit up. Often, they had a nice fire, when the candle flame interfered with the curtains.

So we give a dinner party. Our guests are Uncle Sanyi and Uncle Laci. Uncle Laci is a friend of Mum's from the olden days, the only Hungarian who is poor and can't go to Europe every summer. Uncle Laci kept his morals, which is why he doesn't marry an heiress, although his crown is still pretty good and only slightly worn around the edges. Instead of selling himself, he prefers to be a waiter. Trouble is that at the last wedding Uncle Laci got a little bit tipsy on the champagne and made a pass at the bride. She had no sense of humour, which is why Uncle Laci is unemployed at present.

We have an Imperial Peking dinner, which is cheaper than whatever people used to eat in Hungary, and gives Mum a chance to show off her Mandarin. She's getting pretty good in Mandarin these days, which is why we no longer eat rice, only chow farn. This Imperial Peking dinner we have on Christmas Eve consists of the best and choicest leftovers from last week, such as crisp, roasted chicken skin, chop-suey made of asparagus stalks (the tips we served for salad when Auntie Daisy came and brought the presents) in soy-sauce, and a sweet-and-sour rib, for which Mum made the sauce out of tinned pineapple Gwendy sent me from Hawaii.

The only edible part of our Imperial Peking dinner is the risotto milanese and the cakes Uncle Sanyi brought from Eclair. (When I say, Isn't the risotto milanese good? Mum pokes me in the ribs. Whereupon I correct myself and call it in Mandarin chow farn.) And with the dinner we drink Dad's choicest chianti, which, anybody can tell you, is the proper wine to serve with a Chinese dinner. After all, wasn't Marco Polo an Italian and the discoverer of China?

Now, I am getting kind of anxious for the tree to go up in flames—I mean for the candles to be lit and the presents distributed. While we have our dinner the sitting-room is locked up, and only after the Chinese Nescafé are we allowed to march in, while Uncle Sanyi leads the band and sings "Stille Nacht, Heilige Nacht."

Well, they couldn't have given us a bigger surprise than what greeted us on entering the room. There was our tree, to be sure, lit up by Miss Ford's Japanese candles, but apart from the tree, there was very little else, except the useful gifts like the sweaters Uncle Sanyi gave us, and the camel-hair coat for Daisy from Auntie Daisy. As far as toys are concerned, there was a $2.95 electric train which I saw Dad carry home under his arm one evening—and Nothing Else!

Where are our presents? I yelled apprehensively at Mum. She embraced me affectionately, trying to soothe my temper with a strong whiff of Arpège which I saw her pour over herself in the kitchen on account of the Chinese smell. And Dad, who is a silent man, steps forward and delivers a speech which has a lot to do about Merry Christmas and Let's love each other regardless of Sex, Creed and Race (this dig was meant for Uncle Laci, I bet), but about presents all he has to say is: HE HAS SHIPPED THE PRESENTS BACK TO MELBOURNE ON ACCOUNT OF THE OVERWEIGHT. And we shall receive them next Christmas in the congenial surroundings of our own home, and not in the rented apartment on Claremont where they would be lost.

Now, I call this a dirty trick, and don't worry, I say so. I say plenty, and howl enough to bring the old Prof who lives under us up to see what's going on. Dad gives him a glass of port, which is mud in his eye, naturally. I can tell you, grown-ups are a bunch of cheats and liars, and hypocrites.

Then it's Mum's turn to step forward and she does this with her best foot, which sends Daisy flying to the hall. She yabbers a lot about ungrateful kids these days, who don't appreciate what their parents are doing for them, such as this round-the-world trip which we are at present enjoying. But to show that a mother's heart is full of love and forgivingness, she will not punish us for our behaviour, but give us a colossal present instead.

Hear! Hear! I yell in unison with Uncle Laci, who in the quietness of a dark corner has managed to polish off the last drops of Dad's cognac. Hear! Hear! yells Uncle Sanyi, who believes that for a Kibitz nothing's too expensive.

Well, Mum smiles at Dad and together they give a touching picture of togetherness, while Mum announces that regardless of expense and her feelings for us, she sacrificed her mother's instincts and booked Daisy and me into the most wonderful little place in Switzerland.

77

It's called the Children's Paradise.

It's called that because only children are allowed in there. Grown-ups, especially parents, are forbidden.

We shall get two months of holiday in this quiet, cute little mountain resort, and meanwhile she and Dad will just have to resign themselves to doing without us. They shall make the best of a rotten situation and will tour Spain, which won't be the same as if they had us with them too. And they promise to send us postcards from everywhere they visit, including the bullfights.

Well, this is a bit thick, isn't it? I think the only decent person in our family is Auntie Lilly, who, having had to miss our cheerful Imperial Peking Christmas dinner on account of a tricky confinement, calls on Christmas Day proper, loaded down with parcels. She doesn't let Mum or Dad relieve her of her burden, but distributes them to us herself, while Mum has to swear an oath not to exchange them for anything useful or send them by boat to Australia.

21 *Why they lie to us about Switzerland*

Dᴏɴ'ᴛ let anyone fool you at school. I can tell you. It's a small world. What's worse—it's square too. How else can you explain that you fly from one place straight to another.

You take off in New York, which some people say is America, and fly direct to Zurich. Zurich is in Europe. You fly there direct, and you fly straight. I can tell when a plane is turning around, and this one went straight as an arrow.

We leave New York right after Mum made her debut at the Hungarian ball. It was her last wish, and we let her have it. She cut a fine figure in pale blue tulle borrowed from Auntie Daisy. Her only disappointment, so she told us later, was that the Archduke did not attend after all. Mum was to make her curtsey as a debutante before the Archduke. But in life you can't have everything.

All the way on the plane we are told that this Switzerland is a fairy-tale country. They have this Children's Paradise there, and chocolates made by Lindt and Sprungli grow on trees. When we get off at Kloten I don't see one single tree with chocolates on. But there's a band instead, marching along the tarmac.

Mum loves a good military salute. Which is why she straightens herself out under the weight of five loaded overcoats and four overnight bags as she returns the band's salute, which she claims is for her.

She didn't tell us that Switzerland is a military country. Yet the next thing we see is Uncle Vincent waiting for us inside, in his best Sunday uniform. The Swiss like to play soldiers on Sundays and holidays.

79

Otherwise Uncle Vincent is a Dr. Juris. That means a lawyer. He went to Chicago University the same time as Mum, which was a hundred years ago. Occasionally, he was allowed to take Mum out and buy her a hamburger or take her to a dance. He didn't know then what it would cost him later. Now he can drive us to the Children's Paradise in his Volkswagen. Four of us only, but five suitcases, not to mention the casual luggage such as the stuffed overcoats and overnight bags. He promises to buy a bigger car so he can transport us in comfort next time.

Everything's on time in Switzerland. The plane, the band, and Uncle Vincent. They are reliable people, the Swiss, Mum tells us. They can't afford not to be, or else people would stop buying their watches.

We drive for miles along the country which looks like Bear Mountain Park, only in Switzerland they don't have snow. At least not when we get there, which is in winter. Uncle Vincent says that if we are good, we may stay for a long time, perhaps even until summer. In summer we shall surely see snow in Switzerland. It's a queer place by the first look of it.

They have these little towns, with pot-bellied houses pushing out onto the footpath, and churches with all sorts of tops—some sharp like nailfiles, some round like onions. I am used to Riverside Church and St. Patrick's on Fifth in New York, and Swiss churches are different.

Anyhow, we go through a lot of these places, and a lot more of the country which looks like Bear Mountain Park, until at last we come to a road-fork where we take the steep path to the left. And, lo and behold, there is a hill, and on top of the hill a big red house, which Uncle Vincent tells us is the Kinderheim.

I ask where the Children's Paradise is, and he says, right here, in front of my nose. Well, right here is this red building with a great big barn stuck onto it. The smell is lovely, just like cows. The noise sounds like cows too. The name of the place is Wil.

We stop the car and get out and at the door we are met by a lady in black who calls herself Hanni. I think she is saying to us Welcome to Children's Paradise, because we all shake hands, even though it's hard to understand her language. It doesn't sound English to me.

Uncle Vincent brings up the luggage, but it seems that Hanni doesn't want him to put it by the door. In fact, she begins to talk very quickly, and the way Mum and Uncle Vincent look at each other, gives me the idea that we may have come to the wrong place, and certainly at the wrong time. Later, however, I find out that what Hanni is saying is that she had sent us a cable which we didn't get, where she explained that she couldn't take us on account of the funeral.

There is an awful lot of talking going on right there on the doorstep, with another lady coming out to interpret. Her name is Berti and she speaks a little English. In the end it's Berti who talks Hanni into taking us, because she's keen on bettering up her English and taking lessons from me.

So they let us stay, and it's a great relief for Mum to see Uncle Vincent stagger in with our suitcases, because now she can leave us there and go to Spain to see the bullfights. She gives us nice lipsticky kisses, and waves fondly from the car which disappears before Hanni can change her mind.

And we are left on our own at last.

22 It's worth knowing how to milk cows

I CAN tell you what a Swiss Kinderheim is. It is quite different from what one expects from a Children's Paradise. But you get used to it. If they only told me the truth, I wouldn't have howled my head off the first night. Because now I just love this place and never want to go away, never. I want to grow up and be a Swiss farmer like Fritz. I don't want to take another bath until next Christmas.

I am busy from morning till night. First, you see, we have this funeral. It happens the next day after we arrive. It is a beautiful funeral, the best I have ever seen. People come to see the dead lady from all over the place. They stay a week. We give them cakes to eat, and sausages, and I have to help killing a calf, so we can serve the funeral guests wiener schnitzel with roesti.

And just when they put the dead lady in the ground, the snow begins to fall. I am glad, because she will have a nice white rug to keep her poor dead bones warm. The dead lady is Hanni's sister, and it's lucky for Hanni that I am here, because I can look after the farm while she bakes for the guests.

We have this farm, you see, and plenty of animals. Sheep, which live in a little house all by themselves and whom I feed on dry fodder. Cows, which wear bells around their necks, so we can hear them from a mile. And a horse to pull Fritz's cart, which is heavy on account of the manure. And best of the lot, we have Bless. Bless is a dog, as big as Daisy and very handy to pull my sledge up the hill. He eats snow, and Daisy can ride on his back.

MD.

No sooner did we get rid of the funeral guests than
Mum appears quite unexpectedly. It seems her
motherly conscience must be bothering her. She brings
us a lot of chocolate, and asks if we are happy. I am very
busy just when she comes, what with feeding the sheep
and giving Bless his bone and carrying wood into the
kitchen for Hanni. So I tell her to go and talk to Daisy
who is outside practising on the Schlitte, which is
Schwyzerdütsch to you for sledge.

Well, Mum doesn't get very far with Daisy either. The
kid says Gritzi to her which means Hello. Then she

asks Mum Wie gotz? which again means Howdy? Mum can't speak Schwyzerdütsch naturally, and she and Daisy don't understand each other. So I stop being busy for a moment and interpret. You see, in Switzerland you absolutely have to speak their language, especially when you deal with a dumb animal like Bless, who doesn't respond to English.

Mum tries to talk us into going away with her. She thinks we are unhappy and neglected and miss the family. She says she would take us to Zurich and we could stay in a hotel. But I know she doesn't mean it. Kids are a nuisance when you are travelling. They must have baths, and milk, and hygienic things like babysitters. I tell Mum to go away and send us a postcard next time. She's real relieved, I can tell by the way she flutters her handkerchief in the air as she goes back on the train.

Now, I have a lot of things on my hands. I can hardly cope. First, there is Berti. She keeps nagging me to teach her English. She brings these books like *Alice in Wonderland* and wants me to read it to her aloud. Well, I just tell her finally to quit, because our parents did not send us to this Kinderheim and spend all that money so Berti could improve her English. If she wants to get rid of her accent, I can recommend her at Oxford. They know me there. Dad put my name down at Magdalen the day I was born.

There are a few kids on the premises besides us. Two boys and a girl. One is Gyuri, who is very lucky. He is a Hungarian and an orphan too. We must share our chocolates with him, which hurts. And Urs, the other boy, who tried to stick a knife into me but missed. I was quick with my foot and the knife went into the pillow instead. He is a mixed-up kid, Urs is, on account of his family. You can't help being mixed up in such a case. What his case is, I don't know. But it's mixed up.

Gina is a little girl who cries. She is older than Daisy, which makes Daisy feel so important. She can look after Gina and tell her not to cry and let her have a play with her Hollywood doll. Gina has never been to Hollywood, and she is very impressed. Occasionally, I stop being busy and tell her a thing or two. One has to share one's experiences with others, which is why they have these Kinderheims. You have kids who are may be Negroes, and kids like Gyuri, who is Hungarian. Gina and Urs are Swiss. I don't know what we are, Daisy and I. Guess we must be Australians with wild Hungarian blood.

I couldn't care less what kids are or where they come from, I am so broadminded. Also, being a traveller, I am used to mixing with all sorts. This is why Hanni and Berti are so happy to have me here. To tell you the truth, between us, I really prefer the animals.

Or our tree-house. I've got this tree-house beside the barn, and there I am sole boss. One day I am an eskimo, and pile the snow high on the boards which make up the tree-house. Then maybe I get the idea of being Captain Cook, in which case my tree-house is really a ship, and Bless a savage kangaroo. Sometimes, when I get a bit homesick for New York, I pretend that the tree isn't a tree but the world's tallest building, and the river at the bottom of the hill the East River. I send a lot of postcards to my friends, showing them nice pictures of Switzerland.

It looks as if Mum and Dad are having a good time. Dad is in London and he sent me a picture of the Queen. He says they'll spend Easter in Spain. I don't know when Easter is until we get the chocolate eggs.

They come one day, sent by Uncle Vincent, and Hanni gives us each a piece "z'vieri"—which means Four o'clock treat. And we spend Easter in our magic forest, because Daisy and I are eager to see the deer. Our own magic forest is just beyond the farm, and it's full of deer Fritz tells me, although we only see one, and that looks a bit like a sheep to me. I am not very good yet at nature-study, having got used to living in cities.

Well, all good things come to an end, I mean the snow melts, and the blossoms fall and God expels Adam and Eve from the Garden of Eden. The same with us. One day Hanni gets into the Volkswagen and drives us to Wil to the barber. I am already suspicious, and say so. Then when we have had our hair cut, she takes us to a shop and buys me this scout knife and a watering can for Daisy. She says they are presents.

I don't realise what's up until we get home and there, in the yard, is a shiny big new car, with a nose like a frog's bottom. And sure enough Mum and Uncle Vincent are in the car waiting to take us away. The car is a Citroen Goddess, which Uncle Vincent bought specially to transport us and the luggage.

While we were in Wil getting our hair cut, Berti had packed our suitcases and they are there in the hall. Bless is licking the leather real fondly, crying in between with his great big saucer eyes. And Mum kisses us and yells, Well, darlings, soon we'll be a family again, and Dad's already in Rome looking for a nice little place for us, and don't you look wonderful and so healthy and fat, but what's that smell about you? Mum can never ask just one question, she must find out everything at once. I tell her it's cow smell, and she laughs and says, How delightfully Swiss.

When we get into the car, I am sad, sad, sad. So I ask Gina and Urs and Gyuri to come with us for the ride in the new car. Hanni and Berti take the Volkswagen, and we are off.

In the car Mum tries to make conversation with Daisy, but the kid sits there real dumb. She doesn't even smile. It turns out, you see, that she doesn't understand a word of what Mum's yabbering about, because she has forgotten English and can only speak Schwyzerdütsch. I translate a bit, especially about that promise of an ice-cream for each of us, which cheers Daisy up a little.

It's hard on Mum finding us bi-lingual, which is what Uncle Vincent says we are, except for Daisy, who can only speak Swiss. Mum says a few words in Hochdeutsch, but I can't stand that language. You see, best people don't speak Hochdeutsch. They speak Schwyzerdütsch, which is the nicest language in the world and even dogs like Bless understand it.

Everybody is out on the balcony, waving to us as we walk to our plane. I turn back around before I climb up the steps, and I can just see Hanni's black dress and Berti's glasses, and Uncle Vincent's rain-hat and camera. There is a red pom-pom which must belong to Gina. You should have seen her cry at the airport which is at Kloten, Switzerland.

And next minute the plane is off. Mum says we are flying to Rome to meet Dad. I tell her I spent the happiest days of my life in the Kinderheim, whereupon do you know what she answers? She says, Why don't you write it up for *The Reader's Digest*?

Which shows that parents are incapable of understanding what goes on in a kid's heart.

23 *There's always the trattoria downstairs*

ROME is very antique. As soon as you leave the airport in the bus you see these great big ruins all along the road. Mum's crazy about the aqueducts, which Dad says are only the beginning. They are great big ruins, and if that's the beginning I wonder where it will end.

Well, the Villa Borghese isn't so bad. At least it's not in ruins and it is also a hotel. The funny thing is that I am inclined to get confused a bit in my first hour in Rome. First, the taxi-driver who takes us from the bus to the hotel, shows us a park, and says Ecco li, tzis iss the Villa Borghese. I can't see a villa anywhere, and I know one when I see one. In Australia everybody lives in villas, but they don't have parks. Only a front garden for flowers and a backyard for washing.

And the hotel is also Villa Borghese. But I don't mind it since I like to live in hotels. This one has stones on the floor which make it nice for roller-skating, though cold to the feet. As soon as I get a moment to myself, I unpack my roller-skates, and pronto! I fly off to dinner.

It seems people must have known about our coming, because they are all out to be nice. I mean hundreds of waiters, and maids in pretty white caps, who rush out to make us comfortable. One helps to remove my roller-skates, another ties a napkin around my neck, while I have this special waiter who cuts up my spaghetti, which is much longer in Rome than anywhere else. It is also green. I suspect the cook must have mixed spinach into it and then tried to pretend that it's only green paint, but she can't fool me. Lucky there is plenty of tomato sauce to take the taste away, because if there's one thing that makes me sick it's spinach.

What makes me a little mad is that nobody understands when I ask for something in Schwyzerdütsch. It's very annoying to be in Europe and not be able to talk the same language everywhere. And on top of everything, Mum keeps yabbering in something which she claims is Italian, but which Dad says is Spanish with a Majorcan accent. She can't imagine why everybody answers her in English.

I am all for a United Europe, with Schwyzerdütsch as a universal language!

Dinner takes a long time in Rome. Personally, I am pretty full after my plate of spaghetti, but Dad says, Eat up everything, who knows when you get a decent feed again, what with everything being what it is in Rome. So I must have this thing called antipasto, then these wiener schnitzels which haven't got nice breadcrumbs on them and taste of cheese, and greens that aren't green but grey, and more cheese. Dessert isn't included in the pensione, so when I reach for a piece of cake Mum raps me on the knuckles.

Dad tells Mum that Rome is murderously expensive and the sooner we get into our flat the better. A couple of days at the Villa Borghese, and we would be broke. So right after dinner they decide to put us to bed and go and see the flat. I protest, and sure enough the maid takes my side, which is why I end up going with them, while Daisy stays at the hotel. In Rome you don't need baby-sitters, because Italians have plenty of their own babies and they wouldn't dream of kidnapping us.

As we leave the hotel, Mum gets one foot into a taxi, but Dad pulls her back and explains that, in order to absorb the atmosphere, in Rome people must walk. So we get lost in the Villa Borghese, which is the park this time, and when we come to the gates, we find there's a man already locking up. Dad says they must lock up parks in Rome, because this is a holy city.

Dad is leading the way, which is why I am not surprised that it takes us ages to find the flat. First we go through dark little streets, then we turn into darker and even smaller streets, then we come out by some steps, which take Mum's breath away. She says they are the Spanish Steps, and all her life she lived only for this moment, when she would see them for the first time. She gets so excited, and yabbers so much, that no wonder somebody rings the church-bells just as she falls flat into a flower pot.

You see, they have these steps covered with flower pots, which Dad says is on account of the Azalea Festival. You can't be careful enough how you descend on them, because they are a trap. Besides, it's just dark enough to get thousands of people interested in coming out to see the flowers. It's when Mum makes this mistake of stepping on somebody's pilfering hand that she falls flat into the flower pot. What a city!

Well, walking is out thereafter, and we have to continue in a horse-cab. It's the same type of horse-cab they have in Central Park, New York, only here the streets have these funny little stones for the pavement, which make the cab bounce up and down and make you a little bit sea-sick. Just as I get rid of the antipasto, the cab stops, and there, before our eyes, is a river.

Ah, the Tevere! Mum says, while Dad pays the driver. He has some difficulty with the Roman money, which is why the man follows us all the way inside the big apartment house, shouting at him. In the end, Dad gives him another nickel, and tells him to jump into the river.

The apartment house is right on the river, and even though it's dark, you can still smell that it's old. There is a lift, but when you ring the bell nothing happens. When you ring again, a voice from a distance shouts something what Dad claims isn't nice. He has seen this film *The Bicycle Thieves* and he knows when something isn't nice in Italian. So we take the stairs and climb all the way up. People in Rome must be crazy about steps, which is why they keep their lifts out-of-order.

Well, we find the flat which belongs to a Signora, who calls me Bambino and kisses my hand. Then she forces my mouth open, and just as I begin to wonder if she may be a doctor and the whole thing is a trick on Mum and Dad's part to bring me along so she can see my tonsils, she pops a candy into it and says, Che bello, Mamma mia! The price of the flat has gone up since yesterday, which is why she can afford to be nice to me and give me a candy.

Mum and Dad do a bit of arguing, while I go off and look at the place. Well, you can't see much at night, especially since the lights don't work, but the Signora promises to have the bulbs put back to-morrow, and if Dad only gave her half the rent as a down payment, she could even ring up the electricity people to bring back the meter. But I am glad, because there is a pet turtle in the W.C. which will be nice and handy for Daisy, she won't need a stool for climbing onto the seat. Also a big flower pot, with a tree growing out of it. When Mum pulls the chain nothing happens. But the Signora promises to have it fixed by the morning.

We move in in the morning, at nine a.m. sharp. At daylight the apartment isn't much different from night-time, on account of the lack of windows. You see, this is such an old house, they built it at the time when people were fighting in Rome, so the less windows they had on houses the better. But when they modernised the house two hundred years ago, they put this nice corridor along the flat, which gives you all the air you want, and also a nice view of the landlady's pink underdrawers on the line. Besides, you are kept in touch with all the seventy-five other inhabitants of the Condominio, which means apartment house, because they have windows overlooking our balcony.

The patrona says to Mum that she'll be very happy at the Via di Ripetta. Tradesmen, she says, call regularly. All Mum needs to do is just put her money into this little basket, and lower it down on a string into the courtyard. The tradesman will put the goods into it, and she can pull it up again, which is just wonderful, and how easy to do the shopping. (Give me the A & P any time, but not so Mum. She is in love with Rome.)

We haven't started to unpack yet, when one after the other the seventy-five tenants all make a visit, wanting to have a good look at the Americani, which are us. In Rome everybody is an Americani who has traveller's cheques. You are very much respected, as long as your traveller's cheques last. What Romans hate are Germans and Dutch and Swiss, who come regularly but bring their own powdered milk and Nescafé. They like to sleep outside the gates, and, if their car isn't big enough, they pitch their tents. You can't make a profit on tourists like these.

It was time to have lunch when the last visitor left. So Mum thinks she'll just fry some eggs and bacon. The trouble is that the kitchen is there, but nowhere to cook. Actually, the neighbour who watches Mum busy herself in the kitchen, trying to turn on the tap for hot water, which doesn't work, suggests a good trattoria downstairs. He would show it to us himself, but the trouble is he is engaged at present. You see, our kitchen is the only room with a window. It opens right onto the neighbour's W.C. He's engaged there, but he likes company to talk to.

This is an impossible situation, says Mum, with the result that we have lunch and dinner at the trattoria, and next morning Elena arrives. Elena is going to be our donna.

Dad calls her Elena di Roma. Mum bets that Elena is a tightrope walker by profession. You see, she is just so perfect that you can't help wondering what she must do on Sundays, which are her only days off. She must be a tightrope walker in the Via dei Coronari, the street she lives in.

The only trouble with Elena is that though she can talk she can't read or write. Which makes it difficult for Mum to understand her dialect, as it isn't Majorcan. When Mum suggested she write down her orders so Mum could do the shopping, Elena explained that she can't write. But she makes up for it by talking.

The first time she saw us, I mean Daisy and me, Elena picked us both up and squashed us to her bosom. She has a bosom like an inflated rubber raft. Very nice and comfy. Daisy liked it so much that she decided right there and then that as long as we are in Rome she won't take another step. She lets Elena carry her everywhere.

In the morning we go to the Castello to play. In the afternoon she takes us to the Pincio. In between she cooks dinner and does the washing in the bathtub. Every day she washes, so she can gossip with the other tenants while she hangs out the clothes on the line which stretches from our corridor right across to the opposite house. She uses a long stick to push the clothes out once she has tied them onto the rope.

I bet at night when we are sleeping she walks across the rope to Giuseppe who is the man with the little moustache.

24 *Ruins are provided free of charge*

D<small>AD</small> has his office in a Palazzo. He likes working there because of the lovely naked ladies. The Palazzo is full of them. He even has them painted on his ceiling. He says he's doing comparative work. Mum thinks he must be comparing one lady with the other, taking two different ladies each day. I bet we are going to stay a long time in Rome.

I don't really mind it. I think Rome's the best playground in the world. You see, anywhere else we have to start off by building our own ruins before we can play hide-and-seek. In Rome everything's already provided.

The Castello where we play in the morning is a patched-up ruin. Actually, they say it was built to be a tomb for a dead Emperor. Then the Popes took it over and made it into a Castello. This explains the golden angel on top, whom you can see from every balcony in Rome.

We can't play inside the Castello, because you have to pay to enter. When Auntie Lilly arrived, which was shortly after we moved into the flat, she took us there once. She paid. They have these interesting old jail-caves in the Castello, where people were put to rot away. They were left there for hundreds of years. You can just imagine. Rome's so full of history and old bones you don't know where to begin.

Let me begin with just an ordinary day in Number Settanta Via di Ripetta, which is our address. We get up very early, long before Mum and Dad and before Elena appears, which is eight o'clock. Even the big door downstairs is locked when we get up, because the por-

tiera is still asleep. So what we do is, we go down to the courtyard, then climb up one wall and into the garage, which has its door open on the street.

Giacomo, the baker, is up earlier than us. His shop is in our house. When we arrive, he yells out a Bon giorno Patrizio, Bon giorno Belissima (which is for Daisy). Then he hands us each a big piece of pizza. We sit down and have a yarn with him. It's easy to speak this language in Rome. What we say is Grazie tanti, and the rest he can't understand because our mouth is full of hot pizza. When we finish, we pick up the fresh rolls for breakfast and save him putting them into our basket which Mum forgets to lower anyhow.

After Giacomo we visit Pietro, whose wineshop is next door. Pietro is very fat. He is so fat that he has to hold up his stomach with his hands in case it drops on the floor which is always wet on account of the vino he keeps in his shop in barrels. So we just go in and say Ciau Pietro! or Bon giorno, depending what mood we are in. He pours us each a glass of chianti and puts a spoonful of sugar in to make it sweet. He tests it with his finger which he dips into our glasses. He has fat, hairy fingers with a snake-ring on his little finger.

I can recommend a glass of chianti with a slice of pizza before breakfast. It makes the day for me. I am getting used to it so much that I don't feel like cocoa and rolls any more. It does something for the workings of my *fegato*, this glass of chianti every morning. Fegato is my liver, and everybody can tell you in Rome how careful you must be with your liver. Once I ate too much pasta and my fegato started to grow. It grew and grew and Elena told Mum to call a doctor. He was a specialist and charged Cinquemille Lire. For that he took Mum's pulse by mistake. But Mum liked it. So did the specialist. And soon afterwards my fegato stopped growing, and I was normal again.

Anyhow, I don't take chances with my fegato, so I have this glass of chianti with Pietro. He tells me he's very lonely, on account of his kids, who all live in New York. One is the chief of police there, the other is almost the mayor. But they are ashamed of their old father, says Pietro. Personally, though I don't tell him, I can sympathise with his kids. Pietro wears a leather apron and rubber boots.

I pick up the bottle of vino which Dad requires for lunch. He too can't live without his chianti. Thanks to me, he pays for the cheapest brand and gets Pietro's best. Pietro thinks the cheapest is not fitting for a Professore, especially for an Americano.

When we leave the wineshop, the Signora is just opening the doors of the espresso which is on the corner. So we have to pass through there and, since we are inside, we might as well stay for a little time. We pay our respects to the Signora's pussy, who sleeps on top of a biscuit tin. This is a nice and friendly way to show the Signora that we are interested. In Rome people appreciate it if you are interested in everything. So naturally we get an ice-cream, and sometimes even a misto. A misto is a mixture which we get when we are lucky and get there before the man comes to take back the empty ice-cream barrels to the factory. The Signora scrapes the barrels clean and puts what's left on a plate before us. It tastes like cassata, only better, because of the paper that's stuck to the bottom of the barrel. This paper you can keep on chewing afterwards, and it's like juicy-fruit, made by Wrigley.

Well, by the time we finish our morning round, the portiera is outside the Condominio, leaning on her broom. She is waiting for the art students to come. You see, right opposite our house is this Art School, the biggest in Rome. The portiera is a widow and she likes to be kind to art students, especially young boys. You get kind of lonely when you are a widow, and sailors she would never have in the house. Once a sailor tried to come in after ten o'clock, and you should have heard the portiera. She yelled, What do you think this is? A bordello? Mum says it is. I don't know what a bordello is, but I guess it must be an apartment house with a respectable portiera.

When nobody talks to the portiera, she likes to stop us and tell the story how her husband died. She tells us he was poisoned by his amore with a plate of vitello tonnato. He was no good, bless his memory. Seven years is a long time to be a widow! And to think that all he left her in his will was this pink stone she wears on a chain around her neck. It's called a *corno* and people wear it to protect themselves from the evil eye. The portiera has very interesting stories to tell.

We come home for breakfast, but we don't have much of an appetite. Not like Dad, who asks Elena, Is this breakfast? when she brings him his coffee and rolls in the sitting-room. Elena would not serve him anything else, and certainly not bacon and eggs, which are bad for the fegato.

She takes Mum's in to her on a tray. Mum loves to have breakfast in bed. When she is finished and has made a nice crumby mess, she calls Elena to massage her back. Elena can massage real well, because her other profession is assistant to an undertaker behind the Piazza Navona. Elena's job is to prepare the corpses. She freshens them up first with a bit of a massage, then she gives them a bath and shampoo. By the time the relatives come with the wreaths, they won't recognise the deceased. Elena gets Mille Lira after each corpse.

From us she gets Ottodieci-Mille a month, which is thirty dollars.

Elena can't get to the Castello quick enough with us. You see, she has this bench in the playground behind the Castello, which is her privilege. Romans respect a donna who looks after Americani bambini. I guess Elena loves to take us there, because she can cut a "bella figura" with us. This means showing-off in Italian. All Elena's friends, and nephews and nieces, and uncles and aunts, and Giuseppe Melloni, her amore, come to visit her while she minds us from that bench.

We are the most famous bambini in Rome in June. July we may go to the mountains. It gets too hot in the city.

25 *Aunt Lilly can't sleep on a turtle*

Dad always comes home for lunch and so does Mum. While he works in the Palazzo, Mum visits her Hungarian friends. You don't think there is a city in this world where Mum has no Hungarian friends? Her two closest are the painting ladies. I call them that because they paint pictures. And she has a dear friend who is in the movies. Only he isn't a star. He cuts the film into pieces. Another one is Uncle Hubert, who is a genuine Knight.

Lunch is really dinner in Rome. You eat a lot, so you can enjoy the siesta. Elena cooks a four-course lunch every day, because she tells us that as Americani we owe it to her to feed her in the style she is accustomed to. First Mum thought that a nice plate of spaghetti with a salad to follow would be ideal. Just what the Romans eat, she tells Elena. But to her surprise she has already cooked the vitello tonnato last night and the piselli con prosciuto (which means bullet-peas with ham), and a nice torta big enough for a wedding cake is waiting to be consumed, although the four of us couldn't even finish the pasta.

Pasta is spaghetti. It is also noodles, and bow-ties and snails and ravioli and everything that you eat with tomato sauce, which is called the sugo. Anywhere else in the world people can tell you that a pasta with a nice salad is a meal and a half. Why, Mum serves it all the time when we must have Dad's colleagues from the University. Give them spaghetti, Dad says, when Mum protests. That's all we're going to get when they ask us back, he says. University people have a soft spot for spaghetti. It goes well with the conversation about diapers and measles, Mum says.

Anyhow, what I am about to say is that we come home from the Castello at one o'clock. We walk over the bridge, and we stop at the kiosk on the Lungotevere. The Lungotevere is the Riverside Drive of Rome. In the kiosk Elena buys us each a gelato, so we don't feel too hungry while we wait for the pasta to cook. I like the gelati best on the Piazza Navona, because the man who sells them is Elena's nephew. He's called Alberto. Alberto pushes his ice-cream cart up and down the Piazza Navona. He rings his little bell and yells, Gelati! Gelati! Just like the Good Humour Man in Central Park.

One day, not very long after we moved to the flat in the Via di Ripetta, we are having this ossobucco for lunch. It's this lovely piece of bone covered with tomato sauce, with not much meat around it, which is why I like it so much. You don't have to chew for hours. You just suck the bone and eat the sauce with a spoon. Ossobucco is my favourite.

Well, as I say, we are having this ossobucco, when the door bursts open and in rushes the portiera, shouting and waving her arms in all directions. Elena shouts back, and Dad says, For Chrissake, can't we have peace even during lunch, when a man staggers in, carrying seven suitcases and one hat box which he balances on his head. And behind the man comes our Auntie Lilly directly from New York.

Auntie Lilly was missing us so much that she just hopped on a plane, and didn't even have time to send a cable. She wanted to be a lovely surprise. She was.

We made her bed in the ufficio, which is a cubbyhole conveniently located near the convenience. It has no window, but who cares, Auntie Lilly says. She is very happy to be in Rome, and sure enough we go and have gelati on the Via Veneto.

Next morning when Auntie Lilly wakes up she says she has a pain in her back. Must be the bed, she says. So Mum goes and takes a look at it. She borrowed the bed from the portiera for Mille Lira a night. The portiera told Mum that it's the same bed where her husband met his Maker.

When Mum tests out the bed to see if Auntie Lilly is right, she finds Capriccio in it. Capriccio is the turtle the portiera keeps as a pet. He's very useful for making friends with the students from the Art School. The portiera has him on a lead, and she stands in front of the gate, talking to Capriccio. When a man student comes around, the portiera tells Capriccio what a nice man he is. Whereupon he makes conversation with her instead, because Capriccio is only a dumb turtle.

Mum tells Auntie Lilly not to worry, because the bed is all right once Capriccio is out of it. But Auntie Lilly doesn't like other things either, such as our cold footbath. We have this bathtub, you see, which the landlady bought specially for us. It's the latest in modern conveniences, and the most modern footbath you can find in Rome. Before we came to the flat, the landlady says she had a genuine antique bath in it, which she sent back to the museum. But Auntie Lilly says, How can you lie down and soak in a footbath, especially since you only have cold water.

Actually, it doesn't bother us much that we have no hot water. You don't come to Rome to bath. You come to soak in the atmosphere. What we do is we just fill the footbath once a day, then we have our bath in it in turn. Mum has the first turn, mine is the last. By that time the water is kind of thick. And Auntie Lilly is used to American hygiene.

I forgot to mention that the reason we don't have hot water is not because of the tap. The tap's there, only no water comes out of it. And very little comes from the cold tap, as a matter of fact. You see, we live on the second floor, which explains it. In Rome, if you want plenty of water to come out of the tap, you must live in a basement or at the Hotel Excelsior.

Auntie Lilly doesn't like our best oleander in the W.C. either. She says the leaves are too prickly. So what can we do? We take her to a hotel near the Spanish Steps, where they have a six-foot-long bathtub and plenty of hot water—the first night. The following nights the water gets less and less. But you can't have both, atmosphere and comfort too. At night, instead of taking a bath, the manager suggests that Auntie Lilly should sit on her balcony and look at the floodlit towers of the Trinita dei Monti.

26 *The flea-market and the Cardinal's pillow*

ON Sundays we have this family picnic, you see. It's Elena's day off, and we start with breakfast downstairs in the espresso. There Dad gets out his list of cultural places and reads out the names of the sights we haven't seen yet. There are two hundred and eighty-nine churches on his list, and only twenty museums. When we leave Rome after two months, he still has two hundred and eighty-seven churches and twenty museums, but we can tell everybody that we have been to San Pietro and walked past every museum on foot.

When we have this family picnic, Mum gets in a very bad mood. They argue, and eliminate, and cross off, and argue and eliminate. At last Dad gets fed up, pays the bill and we take a tram. When we don't walk, we always take trams. It's easier to get off a tram whenever there is something interesting to see. Such as this little ruin here, and that rusty Roman sunset there. Or the house where Raphael kept his mistress. Or the trattoria where a plate of spaghetti can be had for Cento Lira. No charge for the atmosphere, and the vino included. Trattoria is a Roman drugstore where they don't serve milk-shakes. They serve vino instead and you can pet half a dozen pussy-cats free. Romans are crazy about pussy-cats, which is why they built those interestingly complicated roofs over each house. It gives pussy-cats plenty of scope to explore the roofs of Rome.

Actually, what we do on Sunday is we visit the flea-market. It's at the other end of Rome and on the other side of the river. You take the tram. You get off once or twice. Once we get off at this convent where Mum says she read they keep these wonderful hidden murals. You can't come to Rome without seeing these hidden murals. So while she and Dad go inside with a nun, we play in the courtyard. They have this old well there, and a ginger cat. What we do is, we put the cat in the bucket, then lower the bucket into the well. By the time Mum and Dad had finished viewing the hidden murals the pussy-cat has drowned. And we can never go back to the convent again.

The flea-market begins with an old gate. They have many of these old gates in Rome. The one I like best is near the Pincio. You go through that old gate to get to the Via Veneto, which is where I like to sit on my free evenings, watching the poodles show off the ladies who lead them on a chain. It seems if you are a poodle and want to walk on the Via Veneto, you must have a lady to take you there. Those ladies who don't have poodles have red Alfa Romeos. They drive very very slowly down the Via Veneto, and often stall right in front of Doney's. Doney's is the place where you can see the best poodles in Rome. They also have these telephones on the table, which are fun. What we do is, Daisy and I, we take separate tables, then ring each other up. Sometimes, when I see a lonely lady who is tired after walking her poodle up and down the Veneto, and is sitting down to her marshmallow ice-cream, I ring her up. I tell her, Would you like to join me at my table and have a banana-split, instead of that lousy marshmallow ice-cream? She says, Sure, honey, and I quickly leave the table and sit with Dad and Mum. You should see the lady's face when she comes over and sees Mum there. As a matter of fact, you should see Mum's face first. She says Dad was making eyes at the lady while she was absent powdering her nose. You can have some fun, I can tell you, and the banana-split costs only six hundred lire.

But, anyhow, I am not talking about the Veneto, but the flea-market. Except that very often when we go there on Sundays, I recognize faces I see around Doney's at night. They are nice, clean American faces. They come to the flea-market to pick up Old Masters. We don't buy Old Masters because we have seen them being made in the Via Babuino near our house. There they make the Old Masters at night, the same that they sell by daytime in the antique shops. Those that don't get sold on weekdays are offered to the Sunday crowd that comes to the flea-market.

Auntie Lilly is a sucker for Old Masters. Why, she almost bought that saint, whose name is Sebastian. She liked the way his poor body was shot full of arrows. His poor body was naked, besides the arrows, because the boys from the Art School who paint these Old Masters don't have money to put clothes on their models. This saint looked like a porcupine at the Bronx Zoo.

One Sunday while we are walking around this dusty old flea-market, I notice a little toy on the ground. He's a priest, and, lo and behold, as I try to walk past him, he talks to me. His mouth opens and shuts and his head nods back and forth. I stop and show him to Mum. She tells me I have an eye for antiques, and starts to bargain with the man, who owns the toy. He has other things too, such as hundreds of spectacles, and a base-ball bat, and two Old Masters hanging from the tree behind his stall. The man who owns these interesting things wears a top-hat. He is eating sardines out of a tin with a hairpin. In the end, he sells us the talking priest for Cento Lira. A bargain, Mum says, when you think that he must be well over two hundred years old.

Once, Mum buys this real velvet pillow at the flea-market. It has the genuine bottom-marks of a Cardinal on the pile. Dad isn't very keen on the pillow, but he can't stop Mum. She is crazy about Cardinals, and doesn't care that the pillow is a bit torn and feathers are coming out of it as we pick it up. Well, as I am writing this book, the pillow is in our sitting-room, and Cyril, my cat, is sleeping on it. He sleeps on his back, because he's a real human cat.

I wonder what the Cardinal who owned the pillow would say about Cyril, my cat?

27 Culture-picnics on the Foro Romano

As luck would have it, we are able to take Auntie Lilly one Sunday afternoon to the Foro. You see, there's just no place to go to in Rome when people are having their siesta from one to four. Even the churches are closed, and the saints have a nap too. But the Foro is open, because it would be unfair to the tourists to prevent them walking on the Sacred Walk from one to four. Sundays, the Foro is simply lousy with tourists.

To go and have a culture-picnic on the Foro, you must first go to the Hungarian cake-shop near the Grand Hotel, which is in the opposite direction, and buy nice and gooey cakes. A dozen of this, a dozen of that, Auntie Lilly orders, same as she does in New York on Seventy-Second Street. Then, because she is a naturalised American citizen who has not walked for thirty years, we get a taxi to the Foro.

The guide-book, which Auntie Lilly carries in her Sak's Fifth Avenue shopping bag, says that the best approach to the Foro is from the Colosseo. So we stop the taxi and Dad pays, but not without reluctance. Auntie Lilly never carries small change like thousand lire notes, and taximen don't appreciate American Express traveller's cheques.

I know the Colosseo inside and out, so I take over from here on. You see, we come here sometimes with Elena when it's a change of air that we need or when her boyfriend, the street sweeper, has his duty in this part of Rome. When I play at the Colosseo I am always Nero, the wicked Emperor. Daisy is a lion who eats up the early Christians, mostly tourists who come to see the place where sacred blood was shed. I explain everything to Auntie Lilly, then take the party across the wide street to the Foro.

You come into the Foro through this great and fancy arch which stands in the middle of the ruins. First you must pay, of course, because it's very costly to keep up these old ruins and the S.P.Q.R. must live too. The S.P.Q.R. is the Society for the Prevention of Cruelty to Ruins. Dad says, it's a racket.

In the olden days famous men rode their chariots through this arch. I like to show things properly to Auntie Lilly, who, I can see, is a bit disappointed with the ruins. She says they make them better at MGM studios. To talk Dad into being my chariot is very complicated. He's just turned his pockets inside out at the paying-gates and is in a bad mood. Besides, the cakes which Mum is carrying are melting rapidly in the heat.

So what I do is, I use my best brains. We are still outside the archway, what with Auntie Lilly trying to persuade us to view the Foro from a distance, rather than walk around the place. Then we could go to a café and send postcards. However, I want to give her a treat, which is why I get this pain in my leg all of a sudden.

I say, Hey Dad, my leg's aching something awful. I can't walk. I must be getting polio! And with these words on my lips I sit down on a nice and flat antique stone on the road.

Well, Dad isn't going to leave it at that. Mum says, Mein Gott! we must run home and put him to bed, and Auntie Lilly being a doctor is busy bending my leg all over the place. I yell. Daisy yells. At this stage Dad can't stand it any longer. He has paid for the whole party to see the Foro, and no polio is going to stop him carrying out his threat. He picks me up there and then, and this is how I ride through the arch of Titus like a famous hero on my chariot!

The rest of the Foro is ruins. You can camp there and have a picnic if you like. However, by the time we find a little shade under three broken columns, the cakes have melted and the best we can do is throw them away. They land on the spot where the vestal virgins kept the Sacred Fire going. But nowadays virgins are hard to come by and you mustn't light a fire on the Foro.

Which is why the idea of a barbecue is out. Instead, we go to Alfredo's to have a bite to eat. Alfredo's is the most expensive place in Rome, but Auntie Lilly says, Never mind, we need to get our strength back after all this culture. Dad waits outside to make sure that Auntie Lilly has got her traveller's cheques.

At Alfredo's you eat pasta just the same as at home. Only the waiter serves it with a golden fork. And there is a nice little Italian gypsy band playing "My Old Kentucky Home", a song that makes us all homesick for good old Broadway and the kids on the block beside Barnard, in New York, U.S.A.

28 *All a-stir in the Via di Ripetta*

Mum rang the Pope, who is the Holy Father, to ask if we could come around and see him some day. That is, to be precise, she rang somebody, who knew somebody, who rang somebody at the Vatican which is the house the Popes built. Now we are waiting for the invitation.

You see, we have seen the Pope once already, but that was only from a distance. It happened when the King of Colorado and Mrs. King, who are friends of Mum and Dad, came to Rome in their new Mercedes. Boy, I love Mercedes cars, they are so ultimately elegant. I took the King of Colorado and Mrs. King to the Pincio, and showed them the Punch and Judy. Then I showed them the naked ladies in the Gallerie Borghese, where I am very familiar with the arts. I often play in the Villa Borghese, just behind the gallery, and I know everybody there. Without me the King and Queen would have been lost.

Then, because they only had a short time in Rome, the Queen, Mrs. King, wanted to go to see the Pope. Mum was able to arrange that too. You see, she used to be a student of the King, when she studied at the University of Colorado. It must have been a funny place, this Colorado. I just can't imagine Kings teaching in the Law School there, especially my Mum. Dad tells me the reason the King has no crown is because he is not a King, only a Dean. A bit confusing.

So Mum arranged this party at San Pietro, which is my favourite church. It so happened that when we went there, there were already two million people present, coming from all over the world. Mrs. King, the Queen, was very pleased to find that Mum has so

112

much influence, because we could just walk into the
church, and lo and behold there was the Pope. He sat
on a big throne and smiled. He waved to me. I waved
back and shouted, Viva Il Papa. I bet he heard my
voice, because he kept looking at that column where I

was hanging from until a gentleman in a red velvet coat removed me.

I would have been happy to leave it at that, but Mum said she isn't going to leave Rome until we meet the Pope socially. It's not good enough just to climb up all those stairs and get onto the roof of the church, anybody can do it. Lots of people did do it, and you can see their names written all over the staircase. Mixed company, Mum says. Personally, I was impressed to learn that lots of Princes and Princesses and Kings and Queens have all walked up those stairs, just to be able to say they had been on top of San Pietro. They have an elevator running for those who can't walk. It costs Cento Lire one way. No wonder Dad made us walk.

I have been under the church too, to see all the tombs and relics and early Christians. My friend, a Monsignore, took us there. He showed us everything and then we had coffee in the Vatican. They have this little tuckshop there, right inside the building, but the cakes are nothing special. The Pope doesn't come to the coffeeshop, which is why we asked ourselves to his drawingroom.

Well, one evening we come home from the Augusteo, which is only one block from our apartment on the Via di Ripetta. We go and play there sometimes, mostly when there is a change in the weather. Elena has trouble with her corns and can't take us up to the Pincio, so we just go around the corner to the Augusteo.

This is an olden-days tomb with a nice, round playground attached. They say it was built for the body of an olden-days Emperor called Augustus. I doubt it, personally, because one day I climbed up the ruin, which is very *pericoloso* and therefore free but forbidden, and squeezed myself through a hole to see what's inside.

Nothing's inside. No Emperor, no bones. Only cats. Millions of cats. You can imagine the rest. We play outside in the gutter. Anybody can tell you that to pick up Italian quick you must play in the gutter. It's good for your accent. Mine is pure Roman.

So here we are, coming home from the Augusteo one night, and who do we see right in front of our house but Mum and Dad, talking real excited to the portiera. It turns out that the invitation to come and see the Pope has arrived while we were out. The reason the portiera is so excited is because our house is four hundred years old, and all that time nobody has ever got a letter there from the Pope.

Well, we go upstairs, and the real fun begins, what with Mum yelling that she has nothing to wear, and people coming in all the time to look at the card. Mum needs all black, she says, and a mantilla over her head, and white for Daisy, and something respectable for me. (Dad doesn't count, he can wear the black suit he had made when he was at Oxford, after all, men's things don't go out of fashion, and his suit is only fifteen years old.)

It isn't quite night-time yet, so we rush out to the Corso, where they have the shops. The Corso is real packed at this hour, which is what I like, because of all the nice and friendly people who pop caramellas into my mouth. Whenever I walk down the Corso I always keep my mouth open so that kind people can fill it with caramellas. We buy a pair of white shoes for Daisy and a black suit made of silk for Mum. The whole thing takes less than an hour and costs only sixty thousand lira—a song. Daisy's shoes take two thousand of that.

When we come home, the flat is full of people. Firstly, there is Elena's whole family with their friends from the Via dei Coronari. Elena is just showing them the invitation. The old Commendatore is down, sipping Dad's secret brandy. He lives on the fourth floor and is a film extra, on account of having no job elsewhere. He was a fascist, Dad says. Luigi, and Pietro from the wine-shop are there, and Signora Spila who leaves the espresso in charge of the ginger pussy, and the butcher who is just arrived with the special order of bistecca, to feed the party.

Everybody wants Mum to try on her frock, and Uncle Hubert arrives, with a small suitcase full of decorations to fix up Dad. There are lovely medals and ribbons in the case, all designed to hide the spots on the suit, and make Dad look like a whisky ad from the *New Yorker*. When he stands beside Mum, she says he hogs the limelight, and is real mad.

It turns out that Mum hasn't anything to wear, the black looks positively dowdy, and what will the Pope say? If only she had a little emerald brooch or something, she could get by, but to go naked like this is heartbreaking. Besides, she forgot about the mantilla, and it's too late now, what with dinner being already on the table, and at least twenty uninvited guests waiting for the celebrations to start.

So, while Pietro contributes two gallons of free chianti, the portiera runs downstairs and brings up her own special mantilla, the same she wore to her husband's funeral, together with a dozen rosaries she would like us to ask the Pope to bless. Mum tries to drape a few of the beads around her, but decides that corals are out of fashion and the mantilla makes her look like the Mona Lisa in mourning.

We don't get to bed until very late, which is when

the last guest leaves the apartment, wishing us good luck and asking to be remembered to the Holy Father.

Dad says, as he surveys the scene and the broken glasses which Elena is sweeping down to the court-yard, I never really thought that Governments come and go, but in Rome there is no doubt, the big boss is still the Pope.

29 Off to see the Pope in private

WE can't go on foot to the Vatican, which is why we take this taxi. The whole street is up and out, although it's not yet ten, and they all wave to us, and yell something that sounds like Auguri.

We drive into the Vatican and the driver circles the courtyard to show the Swiss guard that we are somebody and not just ordinary pilgrims. He wants to charge extra for the ceremonial drive, and I am left to convey to him Dad's feelings on the subject matter, which I do in my best Italian. He tries to follow us inside, shouting a bit, using words that are familiar to me, but send the guard chasing him out of the place. You see, I took a few lessons from the Signorina's cockatoo, who lives on the third floor. So I know what the driver means, and when I translate it to Dad, he goes red in the face. This cockatoo is very clever, by the way. He speaks English too. He can say Loverboy whenever he sees a sailor on the landing.

Dad shows the invitation to a very dressed-up gentleman who carries a gold-knobbed stick. He takes us to the elevators, two of them, and we take our pick. Mum picks the one with a Cardinal inside, to whom she introduces us in Italian. The Cardinal puts his hand on Daisy's head and answers in his best English: Where do you come from folks?

Mum's about to tell him some of our life-story, when the lift stops and the Cardinal rushes out, his red coat flowing behind him, which Mum says is Dior at his best. He is making straight for a door where two Swiss guards give him the first-class salute with their halberds.

We want to go in after him, but the guard puts his halberd across the door, meaning Strictly Private. He doesn't say so, but we can guess from the way he looks. I try my Schwyzerdütsch on him and ask him nice and friendly, Wie gotz? whereupon he points towards the corridor with his halberd. We take the hint and follow the directions.

Here we are, marching down this painted corridor, and every door we try to go in there are other guards, all barring our way. There are plenty of doors, all painted with ladies and flowers and birds, but not one is opened for us.

At last, after walking ten miles, we meet up with a very dressed-up gentleman who waves his gold-knobbed stick excitedly in the air. It seems he was look-ing for us, and we must have got lost, but now he is going to take us straight inside. Prego, follow me, he says.

We enter a big room, just like Grand Central only less crowded. There is a huge carpet on the floor, the same kind we have in our house in Melbourne, only bigger, and it makes me feel at home. There are more guards around, but these ones smile and don't bar our way, so we can proceed from the big room into another big room, and then into a third, and a fourth, etc.

All the rooms are pretty much alike. They have silk on the walls and golden tables with fancy-carved legs. On the tables are always two vases, one right, the other left, and a golden clock in the middle. Monotonous after a while.

At last we come to a room with chairs in, two golden tables and two clocks. In a corner is a great portrait of the Pope propped up on an easel. He looks as if he was painted by Auntie Edith, Mum's painting friend in

Rome. The very dressed-up gentleman tells us to sit down, there are plenty of golden chairs, we can pick and choose what shape we like best.

No sooner do we sit down than a lady arrives, pushing a stroller with a baby in it and carrying a Pan American bag on her arm for the diapers. I can see Mum is annoyed, and sure enough she tells me to find out where she could have a cigarette for her nerves.

So back I go through all those rooms, with Daisy following me, because the kid is scared in this big place. I forgot to mention that I look my best; they really dressed me up for the occasion. I am wearing these grey flannel trousers which Hanni bought me in Wil, and the blue corduroy jacket Auntie Daisy gave me for Christmas. With this outfit I wear a bow-tie from Dad, because my old school tie clashes with the blue of the jacket. And I have this white handkerchief in my breast pocket, which makes me look real classy, especially with my shoes freshly polished by Elena. And Daisy is in her Californian party frock, the same she wore to the cocktail party when they wanted to make her a film-star. She has a veil on her head, and the veil gets caught in every curving furniture in the whole Vatican Palazzo.

We find a Swiss guard at last and I ask him, Please, where can we have a smoke? We are dying for one, I say, on account of that baby they brought inside, obviously to show to the Pope. Well, whoever tells you the Swiss have no humour is a liar, because no sooner do I ask my question there's a whole gang of Swiss guardists around us, and they all laugh until they have tears in their eyes. When a Swiss guard laughs the serviette he wears around his neck shakes like a leaf. They wear these serviettes, you see, in case they mess up their costumes, which are very fancy, all yellow and red, and just a little bit ridiculous. You don't see Swiss men dressed like this in Wil or Zurich. There men wear blue striped suits and stiff collars, which are so tight that it makes them go purple in the face. Here the Swiss have purple legs instead.

I explain in Schwyzerdütsch that it's my Mum who wants to smoke, just in case they misunderstood me. So one of them comes back to the room with us, and shows the way to the smoking-room. We all go, I mean Dad and us, and Daisy and her veil, and we are led through an enormous hall, bigger than anything I have seen in the Vatican.

The Swiss guard tells me that this is the room where the Cardinals come to have a chat with the Pope. You can see their golden thrones all along the two walls, and the biggest throne for the Pope standing in the middle at one end. The ceiling in this room is like a storybook—all pictures. Next door is the smoking-room. It smells real olden days and private, what with stubs of ancient cigarettes put out on the window-sill. Mum says, as she puffs nervously on her Nazionale, that she would not be surprised if a Borgia stepped out of one of the cupboards, the place is just full of history.

These Borgias must be a big family, because you hear a lot about them in Rome. Most of what you hear is top-secret. What I can gather from my friend Mick, the painter who lives in the Via Canova near us, is that there is this Daddy Borgia who likes his daughter so much that he has no heart left for his son. So his son grows up and starts to fight him with his own army, and the Pope shoots back at him from the Castello. I forgot to say that this Daddy Borgia was a Pope, but that he can't help, it's an honour he couldn't refuse.

I

This Borgia family lives in the same palace as the Holy Father, that is the Pope they have at present, who is Pius XII, and not Borgia. You can see the apartment where the Borgias live, if you pay to get into the Museum. I went there once with Auntie Edith, but I didn't think much of their taste. The apartment was kind of bare, if you know what I mean. True, they have all these paintings on the walls and the ceilings, but you get a bit tired of that in Rome. Personally I like to sit down comfortably in a chair and watch TV, and these Borgias have no chairs to speak of, only murals on the walls. No wonder they are a bit repressed and queer.

But I am digressing. This Vatican is a very confusing Palazzo, and your thoughts wander now and then. Well, when Mum finishes her cigarette, and we go back to the room with the baby, we find that we are just on time. There are quite a few people in there, ladies and gentlemen and priests, and a six-foot tall Cardinal, who calls, Attenzione! Please.

He lines us up against the wall, and starts to tell us how to behave, which is to button up and don't molest the Pope, when to my surprise who comes in quietly through a door but the Holy Father himself, in person.

He is dressed all in white and wears glasses. An old lady with her mantilla sitting crooked over her head starts to cry loudly. I am fascinated, and watch the Pope, and he stops first by a priest and they speak, then he stops by a lady and she gives him a present. It's this silver cowboy hat, and I can't imagine what good it is to the Pope. However, he takes it and says Thank you in a language that isn't English, and passes it on to the six-foot Cardinal. This gentleman holds the present carefully, then turns it upside-down to see the hall-mark. I think it's real silver, because he keeps it. Mum says later that it was meant to be an ash-tray and people have worse taste than she credited them with.

But the Pope just smiles, and there he is talking to Dad. First he gives him his ring to kiss, and Dad kisses it, whereupon the Pope asks Dad in English who he was, and Dad tells him, briefly, of course. The Pope says, Very good, very good, and before I have time to kneel down there he is right in front of me. He puts his hand on my head and asks if I was Paddy Donovan, from Australia. Now, I call that being famous, and I am so stunned I don't know what to say, so I just take the ring and have a look at it, then kiss the Pope's hand, which smells good, like freshly ironed linen.

The ring he wears is very big and dark, not quite black and not really blue, just in-between. Daisy, who is beside me, is now smiling at the Pope, and all's well, and I can see Mum leaning forward anxiously, because she told Daisy not to show the Pope her best lace-trimmed petticoat, which she likes to show to strangers. Thank God the kid remembers just in time and before she makes a spectacle of herself, and the Pope says, How old are you? in English. Whereupon Daisy says real loud, Three and a bit, and this makes the Pope smile even more, and he turns around and tells everybody present, This little girl is not quite four, can you imagine? The Cardinal nods his head, and, when the Pope finishes with the people, rushes over and grabs us both by the arm. He puts us right next to the Pope, and we get our photo taken, with me and Daisy and the Pope, and a few others. Unfortunately, another lady, who couldn't stand Daisy being more important than she, puts her face right before mine and says something to Daisy, which is why I don't show too clearly on the picture, but never mind.

The main thing is that we have met the Pope. And do you know, as he walks out of the room, and people cheer him and shout, Viva Il Papa, he turns around and gives us a special wave, and says to the Cardinal, These bambini are nice.

And I now have this coloured photograph in my room, and I can see it every morning when I wake up. I must say that Old Mum looks pretty good on the picture too, what with her mantilla and Dior-model dress, but there is no question about it, the star is Daisy.

She and the Pope are the only ones in white. They both look real smart, and I am glad for the sake of the family.

30 *Soft seats and Third Class company*

WE have been so long in Rome that it's time we took a nice little quiet holiday away from the sights. Mum wants Capri or Positano on account of our health. Sea air, she says, is wonderful for kids. Besides, they have this painting school at Positano she read about in a magazine, and Mum wants to take up art. She hasn't got very far with her Oriental cooking book, because in Rome few people converse in Mandarin, and she could get no practice.

Dad says our visit to the Pope left him bankrupt, what with Mum's black model and the coloured photos, and for once he takes some Hungarian advice which comes from the painting ladies. It appears they have their own private and secret place in the mountains, where they go each year. It's so idyllic there that for the price it would cost us a week in Capri, we can have a month in Funes.

So we get on this train right in the middle of Rome. It's one of those trains with First Class and Second Class. Dad tries to find the Third Class, but Europe being democratised, they have done away with wooden seats. What you get now is Third Class company on soft seats.

I love trains. Never been on one before, but I must tell you, it's even more fun than flying. You can get gelati and salami sandwiches, they bring them to you on a little trolley-cart. And at every stop someone interesting gets on, like the Signora who came and sat beside me. She brought her chickens with her in a basket because they needed a holiday.

When you travel in Italy you see a lot of sights free. Such as these castles they have on top of every mountain, and robbers and knights-in-armour (who can be imagined), and churches and Florence and Uncle Max. We get off in Florence which is Firenze, just to see Uncle Max, who comes all the way from Chicago and hasn't seen Mum or Dad for years. They have this very funny bridge in Firenze (Florence) where you can buy jewellery and souvenirs. Otherwise, it's a very hot place.

We only stay a day, then we get on the train again. Dad says we are going to the Dolomites, which is like Switzerland. I don't believe him, because in two hours you can get to Switzerland from Rome, and we have been on this train for ages and ages only to find, as we get off at last, Auntie Edith and Auntie Ilona yelling happily to us in Hungarian. They kept a nice warm seat for the four of us on the bus, and we take turns, two at a time, until we come to Funes. The rest of the passengers make it a crowded trip, what with the roads curving and all that, and Daisy being sick at every bend.

Auntie Edith and Auntie Ilona are the painting girls. To make it sound easier, Mum calls them Les Girls. It seems everybody knows them in Funes, and the whole town is out to welcome us, which is twenty people. Les Girls, I am afraid, have different ideas about an idyll than Mum.

We go to the town's best hotel which is called the Albergo Agnello. However, as soon as I open my mouth in my best Italian and say *Buona sera,* Les Girls clamp down on me, and say, Hush! You mustn't speak Italian here. Seppe, the owner, doesn't like Italians, which is why the Albergo is called Gasthaus and we have wiener schnitzel for dinner.

I am really confused. Dad says we are in Italy. The place looks like Switzerland. If I speak Italian, people get mad. If I speak Schwyzerdütsch, they don't understand. I wish the problem of South Tyrol would be settled one way or other. I prefer countries with a King.

But the atmosphere is very nice. We have a room to ourselves, Daisy and I. And no bathroom. From the

window we can look across to the pig-sty. A big tree
shades the pig-sty. We have breakfast under this tree,
and sometimes when Seppe isn't tired he serves us
lunch there too. The pigs grunt a bit, because they don't
like guests to disturb their privacy.

Behind the pig-sty is a meadow full of daisies. And
behind the meadow are the mountains. The hotel has
its own little church, which we can see from the balcony when we go to the W.C. The church is white,
with a red onion roof. Above the door somebody
painted an angel with a sword in his hand. The door is
always locked. When it rains, the blue runs from the
angel's wings.

My best friend is Peter, who wears shoes only to
church on Sundays. He is lucky. His father is a horse-
shoe-maker, which is why Peter doesn't have to have
shoes when we play.

31 *Saving money is easy in the Dolomites*

I AM crazy about Funes. So much to do all day. For instance, in the morning Frau Marie comes and knocks at our door. She brings the water up in a jug. Sometimes we wash our hands in the china bowl, sometimes we just sail our boats in it.

Before breakfast, we have a few words with the pigs and the other animals. They understand Schwyzer-dütsch, so it's easy. Then we have hot chocolate under the chestnut tree, and when we finish, Dad gives me lessons in English. He says I can't spell. He also says I can't read.

The trouble is that he just doesn't know how to teach. He gets mad and pulls my ears. Of course, I wouldn't learn from him anyhow. Just because he's a Professor, he thinks he can boss me around.

After my lesson Dad goes to the hotel which is right next to our Gasthaus. He likes variety, he says. So he takes a seat under another chestnut tree, and orders himself a cup of Italian coffee. No sooner does it arrive than Mum and the painting girls appear. So he orders coffee for all of them, moaning about the cost of living.

When Auntie Edith is finished, she goes upstairs and makes their bedroom into a studio. Then she calls me for my sitting. You see, I have my portrait painted by Auntie Edith, who is very famous.

For my portrait, I wear these blue jeans, and my red jumper from Uncle Sanyi. I lick my hair down with water, and, pronto, I take up my stand in front of Auntie Edith's green dressing gown. It hangs from a hook on the door, and she says the colour contrast is just terrific. While she paints, Auntie Ilona lies down on the bed and tells me stories. She has very good stories, all about famous children, such as a boy called Mozart, who plays the piano when he is six, and an Italian boy called Michelangelo, who is just crazy about painting and doing sculptures.

Personally, I think these boys are being exploited by their families. I myself can paint and do absolutely everything, but I just wouldn't do it on order. Though I don't tell this to Auntie Ilona, because she is a little bit old, and very keen to make me into a famous artist. She says ordinary people are dull, and God forbid, Paddy, she says, that you grow up an average citizen.

Which is why when my sitting with Auntie Edith is over, Les Girls take us on an educational walk in the country. There are three very important churches, and every day we do one or the other over. We look at them from the valley and measure the perspective. Then we climb the hill, and look at the nice Gothic stonework which is just a bit ruined. Then we ask the farmer for the key, go inside and listen to a lecture by Auntie Edith who can get very excited over the same old thing every time we give her a chance. What she likes best is this wooden altar which can be opened and shut and is pretty crowded with wooden figures who are all the same. They are old and cross-eyed and painted gold and red and blue, and absolutely and marvellously Gothic.

Thank God there are only these three churches in the whole countryside. I like best the one which is very, very far from the hotel, because to walk there we can follow the little stream and pick strawberries. Auntie Edith gets excited about strawberries, because their shape is absolutely and marvellously Gothic. This, however, doesn't stop her from eating half the bucketful I pick.

As I said before, we have lunch sometimes under the chestnut tree. When it's lunch-time, every bell in every church begins to ring. And Peter is sitting over the fence, waiting for me to finish with my Salzburger Nokkerl, which are dumplings that stick to your stomach and make you feel so full that you think you are going to burst.

I love the afternoons best, because then the grown-ups leave me alone. Peter knows all the exciting places in the mountains, such as where the blueberries grow, and where we can find mushrooms, and where this farmer chopped up his wife with an axe. He never takes the road, we just shin up the steep side of the mountain, and when we have picked our berries, we eat them straight away. Then we just lie on our side and roll all the way down to the butcher's paddock—oh, I love it so much!

Daisy's legs are too fat, which is why we don't take her with us. She goes with Mum and Dad, or with Karli, who is Seppe's son and wears red pants and pokes his nose. He has a baby brother, Franzili, and on Saturday night Mum borrows Franzili's bathtub so she can give us a good clean-up. The rest of the kids in town have the whooping-cough.

We have dinner in the Schenke, which is the big room downstairs. Usually, it's full of men who just sit by the tables all day and half the night, drinking wine. They smoke these funny long pipes, and never say a word. Seppe says they are the farmers from the neighbourhood. In Funes the work is done by the ladies, who cut the hay with these sharp scythes and sweat like mad. The farmers only go home for dinner, and afterwards they come back to the Schenke.

After dinner, Seppe and I beat Dad at table-bowls. It's real easy, all you do is you put this board on the table and stand up the figures, then you get this twirler and twirl it with your thumb and forefinger. The twirler twirls along the board and knocks the figures down. You get three turns. I knock them all down in one. While Dad takes Daisy upstairs, I have a quiet drink with the farmers. I drink raspberry juice flavoured with wine.

Les Girls and my parents play bridge every night in the Schenke. Dad says, No holiday in the Dolomites is complete without having at least two Hungarians. Two and two make four, and you have a game of bridge. Seppe turns the lights out at ten, because the river, which makes the electricity, is very expensive.

We are very famous in Funes because we are the only guests in the hotel. Nowadays, Seppe says, tourists come in their own caravans, and their meanness kills the trade. Seppe wants to go to South America and be a headwaiter, so he can wear his dinner-jacket without getting laughs from the locals.

In Funes you absolutely must wear leather pants and a Tyrolean hat and walk with a stick. You can buy nice sticks with souvenir medals stuck on to them at the store. You can get licorice there too, and salami, and flypaper. What you can't get is balloons and paper hats for a birthday party.

Which is why Daisy's party in the Schenke was not a real success. We had a gooey chocolate cake, and hot chocolate and no hot-dogs. No hats, no balloons, no crackers. Wish Dad hadn't been so mean in Rome, where you can buy all the balloons in the world from the man who sells them on the Pincio. He has two million balloons all blown up and he holds them by their strings. He yells Ballucini, ballucini! and when there are no customers hops on his Vespa and drives around in circles, with the balloons flying behind him like mad.

For Daisy's birthday Dad gave himself a walking-stick, which he cut from a bush. It's silly and twisted, and when we walk down the main street in Funes everybody looks at us. I bet they think we are tourists, on account of Dad.

On Sundays we get all dressed up and walk up the path to the biggest church of all three. Boy, you haven't seen dressing up if you didn't go to church on Sunday in Funes. The farmer-ladies wear this costume in black, with aprons in front and these funny old hats which look like a slice cut out of a black stove-pipe. They have ribbons on their hats and you can tell from the ribbon whether they are married or just ladies. Very simple.

After church we come down the steps and visit the churchyard which is right beside it. This churchyard is very nice, like a sort of telephone book with names and numbers on every cross. When you get bored, you take yourself to the Kabis, which is a real tourist hotel with baths and umbrellas and German number-plates on Mercedes cars. We don't mix with these tourists, because we are locals who live in the Gasthaus in the valley, but the ice-cream is nice.

The day before we leave Funes we go to the Kabis to have a family bath-party. Then, as we are nice and clean, and nobody knows we all used the same water, Mum takes us to the store and buys us each a Tyrolean hat, and a few yards of this material with red hearts on which she will have to have made up for matching dirndls for Daisy and herself.

So if you want to go to our place and have a rustic holiday there next year, just take a train from Rome which goes straight to Chiusa in only ten hours. There you get off and stand on the corner, until Anton's Dad, who is the bus-driver, comes. He gives you a ticket on the bus to Funes, which you can't mistake once you come there.

Seppe will wait at the bus-stop, wearing his green apron, and he'll take your luggage and show you the way across the street to his Gasthof. He'll say: Gut'n Abend, meine Herrschaften, which, just in case you don't understand him, means Hello and Welcome to the Gasthof zum Lamm.

32 *Between Rome and Hong Kong is a sheik*

IT's easy to go from Funes to Hong Kong. We take this train, you see, to Rome, and we take this plane in Rome— Buona sera. And while the plane is a few hours delayed at Ciampino airport, we go back to Rome, because we have forgotten to throw our coins into the Trevi Fountain. It doesn't count unless you throw your coins in there. Personally, I have seen this fountain hundreds of times, and used to wade in the water with the other kids, but we must go back and stand with our backs to the old statues, and throw our coins in so we can come back soon. I throw a nickel in and Mum her last Swiss franc, while Dad takes our photo for the album.

And when we turn around there is this great big statue of an angry man, all lit up, and, lo and behold, he strikes water from the rocks and looks at us so cross for having thrown in foreign currency that I slip him my last Cinquanta Lira just to be able to come back and face him again with a clear conscience.

And half an hour later our plane takes off for Hong Kong.

It takes a long time to get to Hong Kong, because now and then we stop and get out of the plane, mostly at nights. The first place we get out is very exciting, especially since a soldier is watching over us with a tommy-gun in his lap. He makes sure we all get our yoghurt, and don't peep out at the airport which is dark. Dad says, This is because of the Middle East crisis, but I don't argue with him. I hate yoghurt at night, but what can you do?

Then we get off to have a glass of warm orangeade. Personally, it's a crazy idea, when the plane has more orangeade than you want, and nicely iced. Just because there is a sheik in a dirty old bathrobe, sweating in the airport lounge, they make us get off to see him. The heat is intense, although it's only midnight. The sheik is sweating because he is used to his air-conditioned Cadillac. He doesn't have to pay for petrol, because he drills it himself. The place is called Bahrein, if it means something to you.

Then we get off again to take a look at some ladies who wear all-coloured nightgowns and red spots on their foreheads. At least the orangeade is iced, and if you want a feed, just say so, and a man with a turban will bring it pronto. It tastes like Hungarian goulash. The place is India.

After India, we go to sleep. Daisy snores because she can't get comfortable, with this Indian gentleman sitting right next to her and removing her foot every time she puts it in his lap. This gentleman has his handkerchief full of precious stones, which he shows to Mum. But before Mum can pick out this nice green stone, Dad leans forward and explains to this Indian gentleman how much money he owes to his bank manager. He calls it overdraft, which means that the numbers are written in red ink. Very special, and only the best people can afford to have overdrafts. So the Indian gentleman ties a knot in his handkerchief and puts it back in his pocket.

I don't really sleep, I just pretend to, because I don't feel like eating the fried egg the hostess brings around for breakfast. The Indian gentleman eats his with his fingers, and a big precious stone sparkles on his crooked little finger. I think he must be a magician.

And so we come down from the sky to Hong Kong.

Hong Kong is bigger than any Chinatown in the world. It's a whole island, and a big piece of land, a lot of sea, and boats everywhere in the harbour. Best people live on the Peak, and tourists live in the Peninsula Hotel across the Peak.

We don't stay at the Peninsula Hotel because we have an invitation. We go and live with Auntie Helly, who is almost Hungarian and therefore socially acceptable. She is one of Mum's best friends and actually Viennese.

We cross the harbour in our car and not even the fenders get wet. This is because we drive the car on the ferry and the ferry takes us to the main island. I stand by the rail and watch the ships. You see all sorts of ships, many you have never seen before. Such as what Auntie Helly calls sampans and junks. They are ships for Chinese people, who live on them. They have sails that are all patched up and look like my quilted bedspread at home. The Chinese row them with long poles, standing aft and swinging their bodies back and forth. This rowing is done by ladies. You can tell from the babies strapped to their backs.

It's hard to tell a lady in Hong Kong, because most of them wear trousers. They look like pyjamas really. Pyjama-ladies are poor and can't afford nice curves. But there are other ladies with curves high in the front and low in the back and they wear funny frocks, real tight and sticking to them in the heat. They like to air their legs which is why the frocks are slit open at the sides up to their panties. It's very hot in Hong Kong. I wonder why they don't open their neck instead; they wear these stiff high collars all buttoned up which makes them

look like giraffes. Except that their curves are in the wrong places, these ladies could easily be giraffes.

Ladies who wear black and white pyjamas are called the amahs. They push nice high English prams, or take the dogs for a walk. The legs of their pyjama pants are very wide, and their hair is done in one long black pigtail. You can't hear them walk, because they have these black slippers, and sometimes you jump when they come up silently behind you and say, Massa Paddy, want to go take Johnny for a walk. Johnny is the most beautiful Boxer in the world and he belongs to Auntie Helly.

Amahs have gold teeth in their mouth so they can have a sparkling smile. They are really the paid help. Only in Hong Kong head-amahs have amahs who work for them. Such as A-Yin, who has an amah to mind her little boy while she works for Auntie Helly. Besides A-Yin, there is a special amah for Johnny and his sister Piccoletta, and a special amah for Daisy and me.

A-Yin lives under the house. She has this boy called Haiman aged four. A-Yin pays for a blue amah to look after Haiman. Amahs' amahs don't wear black and white pyjamas, they wear blue instead. When an amah gets very, very old and can't work for English people, she takes a job as an amah's amah. This is Hong Kong.

Mum says she would rather have an amah than her Bendix washing machine. What's more, she would throw in her Mixmaster and vacuum cleaner or give them to the Salvation Army, if she could only take back an amah to Melbourne. But we can't, because of the White Australia Policy.

You see, where we live in Australia, we have a high living standard. Everybody has a washing machine and a Mixmaster and can do the work for herself. To let amahs in would lower the standard of living. Which is why they don't let other races in, except white people.

Mum doesn't think much about the high standard of Australian living. She says that what gets her mad is that everybody is as good as the person next door, that is, everybody can get by without amahs. And the plumber who lives next to us is much higher class than Dad, who is a Professor, because he earns twice as much and can spend it all on the races.

When I grow up I shall be a plumber.

MD.

33 There's nothing like a good Chinese funeral

AUNTIE HELLY lives halfway up the Peak. This Peak is a big rock plumb in the middle of Hong Kong. When you build a house on the Peak, first you must get the coolies to take away the rocks and the stones.

From our window we watch these fifty coolie ladies carrying rocks all day. They have long poles which they put across their shoulders. To each end they tie a rock. Then they sing. Some have babies, and they carry the baby on their back. The sun is very strong, so the coolie ladies wear these big straw hats with black frills, just like lampshades.

The Tee-Da-Ying man comes every morning before breakfast. We wait for him in the street. He smiles with his silver mouth and squats down on the doorstep. He takes this big black kettle from the pole and lets us smell inside. The food is delicious. From a basket he gets a bowl, pours water into it, then rinses it a bit and splashes the water over the steps. This way the bowl gets real clean and hygienic. He fills it with food and lets us use his own chopsticks. The whole cost is ten cents. It tastes better even than A-Yin's Yorkshire pudding which is Uncle Jim's favourite food in Hong Kong. The Tee-Da-Ying man makes his own sauce from flies, tomato sauce and melted shoe-polish. Everybody can tell it's very good for you. And much more exotic than porridge. You don't come to Hong Kong to eat porridge for breakfast. You can get that at home.

It's always nice and hot in Hong Kong, except when we have a typhoon. Then it's windy and hot, and you mustn't go outside. You can play mah-jong on the verandah with Number Two Baby Amah. Or scratch

Johnny or pick his fleas. I love Johnny. He is bigger than Daisy and has a real lovely face, with a mouth which dribbles all the time, especially when he comes to my bed and puts his face on my pillow.

In the morning A-Yin fills the bathtub, because in Hong Kong we have no water after nine o'clock. This is because of Red China. Personally I can't understand why they have to go and beg water from Red China when there's all this sea around the place.

Anyhow, when the bathtub is full, Johnny goes and lies in it for hours. He lies there for a long time, then comes out, shakes himself dry and lies down on the tiles, pretending that he is a bath-mat. When you have to go to the bathroom urgent, you step over Johnny on the way to the toilet. He doesn't mind. He likes to be a bath-mat and feel he is useful. During the day if somebody wants a bath, he must take it with Johnny or ask him, Please, would you get out, so I can have a bath? If he is in a good mood, he does what you ask him, if not, you will have to squeeze in beside him. The water is full of his hairs anyhow.

Johnny's sister Picco has no personality, on account of being an imported show-dog from London. She suffers from the climate here, because she isn't used to the colonies. Nowadays, every Englishman or English Boxer dog can tell you that the colonies aren't what they used to be. Maybe, if Picco would care for a game of mah-jong, she could put up with the colonies. Ladies who come from England play mah-jong from morning to night. It takes their mind off the climate and the servant problem. It's a big problem this, because you just have to put up with two or three servants, and no good crying after Mrs. Morrison, who is a gem and does for you once a week in England.

Auntie Helly doesn't like mah-jong which is why she has this boutique downtown. There she sells mah-jong-ladies models and cheongsam-ladies models made by her own private M. Dior. M. Dior is from Shanghai and has proper gold teeth. He comes to the boutique every morning to take home the orders and the measurements. Then in the afternoon he returns with the finished model.

Trouble is, Auntie Helly has her own private M. Schiaparelli, too, who is from Peking. M. Dior and M. Schiaparelli are awfully jealous of each other. They are rivals. To watch over them, Auntie Helly has engaged a special sales lady, who does nothing else except stand in the corridor, making sure M. Dior and M. Schiaparelli don't meet each other on the stairs. The boutique is air-conditioned.

Uncle Jim is Auntie Helly's husband and English. He builds boats. Yachts, they call them here, and he starts building a new yacht for himself every six months. He starts right out on the verandah. At the moment, Uncle Jim has this finished yacht, *Helena*, which is the most elegant yacht in the Yacht Club. We take her out and go sailing all over the place. There's a permanently built-in Chinese boat-boy who runs the yacht. When you want to go sailing, you just tell the boy to get the ice. Then we are off. The yacht also has a double bed, single beds for us and all mod. cons. The boat-boy does the washing up.

When we don't go sailing or fishing, we go to Deep-water Bay which is on the other side of the island. We like swimming here better than with the crowds at Repulse Bay beach. After our swim we go to the Lido for an ice-cream soda. The Lido is full of tourists. They come to Hong Kong because they read this book called *The World of Suzie Wong.*

Sometimes we drive to Aberdeen. It's not the same place, Dad says, as Aberdeen, Scotland. No. It's very different. Here the poor Chinese people live on their boats. You see at least two million sampans and junks, all so close to each other that you can jump from one to the other and not get your feet wet. You would never believe me if I told you how many people can live in a sampan. At least thirty. Chinese people, when they are poor, have a lot of children. They all live on board, and some die there too.

I love a good Chinese funeral. Better than the one I helped with at Wil, St. Gallen. You see, a Chinese funeral is a good, noisy party. They have this orchestra which makes a big din. Then they have this corpse. However, he isn't just a plain ordinary corpse. His relatives let him have all his toys and possessions with him on the hearse and they dress him up elegantly for all the world to see. Then they make a procession. Funny to see, sometimes very old corpses have toys with them. Such as Model T Ford cars made of shiny cardboard paper, and little toy houses, or even Cadillacs and Silver Cloud Rollses. All paper, of course.

Dad says that when a Chinese dies he wants to have his car right handy by his side, never mind if it's of paper. The main thing is not to walk all the way to Heaven, because he'd lose face with his ancestors.

Every day there is at least one good funeral in Hong Kong. Daisy and I often take part in the procession. Whenever the people stop, we stop too. We get food. And what food! Better than anything I ever had at the House of Chan in New York with Uncle Sanyi. I love these lovely rotten eggs, which are black. They taste like nothing on earth. They taste real rotten.

When the funeral is over they burn the toys and a lot of Chinese paper money, which you can purchase specially for funerals at these funeral fun-shops in Wanchai. First, when I thought they were burning real money, I ran to get a handful. It turned out, however, that the money was just ordinary paper. Don't think Chinese would burn real dough! Not them. They are old-fashioned where money is concerned.

I could go on living in Hong Kong forever. I just love this place. Personally what I find so nice about travelling is that every place gets better than the last. In Hong Kong they have the best toy-shops in the world. You get bigger cars for a dollar here than what you get for twelve ninety-five at Macy's.

It's the competition that does it. In Hong Kong you can get everything. Only you must keep your eyes open and be sharp. You see, there are these things Made in Japan. They are not made in Japan. They are made in China or in Hong Kong. Then you find things with Made in Hong Kong written on the back. These are the ones made in Japan. What the Japanese do, they make these things, then send them to Hong Kong to have them stamped.

Once you are sharp you can't be fooled. For instance, Made in England is sure to be Made in Hong Kong. You get a suit for twelve dollars in Hong Kong and the tailor comes to your home with all the material in the world, stamped Genuine Made in England. He asks, Master, you in hully? So you say, Yes, and he goes away. Next minute, he's back. He carries this Made in Bond Street, Savile Row, Paris, suit on his arm, ready and wrapped in pink tissue paper.

Dad says they do the trick by overpopulation. Even babies are made in no time in Hong Kong. This is why this is such an important port of call for sailors. I am taking Chinese lessons from the travelling teacher who comes with his chair each morning and waits for pupils in the lobby.

34 *Handling a cheongsam in Macao*

WHEN you get the feel of Hong Kong, you take a ferry and go to Macao. Personally, I can recommend the *Fat-San*. It hasn't been held up for three months. This because the *Fat-San* has only one unbroken gramophone record. It's "Love is a Many-Splendoured Thing". The loud-speaker sings it for four hours, which is how long it takes to go to Macao. Red Chinese gunmen can't stand "Love is a Many-Splendoured Thing". Gives them the creeps. Which is why they don't come near the *Fat-San*.

Of course, besides the gramophone the ferry also has sharp barbed wire all over the rails and the gangway. It looks like a porcupine from a distance. But tourists love the thrill. And that little Chinese statue of a war-rior up the poop, who carries a bloody sword in his hand. He grins so fiercely that bandits get frightened away.

My family goes real crazy in Macao. As soon as we dock, they get into a rickshaw, against all Mum's prin-ciples. But you can't let the poor coolies in Macao starve for their opium all day, waiting for discriminating customers. The trade is slack at present, anyhow. So we take this rickshaw or tri-shaw, I mean all four of us, and make him peddle to the Pousada. The Pousada is a hotel where you can get everything Made in Portugal. They are cheaper even than things Made in Japan, which is suspicious to me. However, Dad, who is a connoisseur, says that the wine is real Portuguese, he can tell by the bouquet. I drink Coca-Cola which at least I can trust.

Daisy and I make friends with Angelo, the cook, while Mum and Dad dress for dinner. In the colonies you must dress for dinner. Angelo cooks outside in the street on the same portable barbecue which Auntie Yvonne has on her patio in Beverley Hills. In Macao you can't cook in the kitchen on account of the heat. If you think it's hot in Hong Kong, try Macao for a change.

We eat barbecued chicken in the courtyard, and watch the Macao ladies and gentlemen make love on the boardwalk. The hotel has a low fence. There is always moonlight in Macao at night.

You come to Macao to play fan-tan, that is, gamble. This is real easy, and open twenty-four hours a day, bring the children, please. Personally I didn't care for this cheongsam Chinese lady who sat in my lap. She smelt Bourjois, which Mum says is a perfume. I told her I am not interested, I only came to play fan-tan.

The way to play this fan-tan is to go upstairs and sit down and lean over the balcony from where you can look down on the table. What you see on this table is millions of pyjama buttons, white plastic, not mother-of-pearl, on account of the civilisation. Two holes in each button, but that's beside the point for fan-tan. You need the holes only if you sew on the buttons, which you don't while you play.

What you do is, you put your money and combination into this basket beside you and lower it down on a string. There two Chinese gentlemen are waiting to grab your basket, and they know what to do with the money. They shuffle the buttons a bit, so you may win first. It's very important to win first, because if not enough tourists come to Macao to gamble the whole island goes broke. And once this happens, the Red Chinese will march across the river and help to put Macao on her feet again, which everybody knows is the end, of course. You can see the flag of Red China from your hotel window.

During the day if you don't play fan-tan you can go up to the old Fort. This gentleman, who is a very important man in the colony, comes and takes you there in his car. He speaks very good Portuguese and tells you everything about the old Fort. Also about the old churchyard and Sir Winston Churchill who has his ancestor buried there. A Churchill is always good tourist bait.

Personally, I find that Macao looks a little bit like St. Gallen, Switzerland, where we once went in Hanni's Volkswagen. Only they have no snow here. But the buildings are funnily like those in St. Gallen. Mum says that's because they are olden days and baroque. Churches have the same onion-tops and big doors with curves and saints who twist their necks rather than see the goings-on. If they saw, they'd die of shame. Maybe also they cannot read the Chinese signs, which is what makes Macao so different from St. Gallen, Switzerland.

In Macao everything's written out in Chinese, and the shop-signs look odd with the iron balconies where you see ladies peeping through the shutters all day. At night these ladies come to the Pousada in their mantillas, so that tourists can see straight away that they are Portuguese pioneer ladies, real class, and not cheongsam.

Mum says, Macao is a lot of chop suey with baroque trimmings. Which is why I have to teach Angelo, the cook, how to barbecue hamburgers. He wants to go to Los Angeles, Calif., and work in a drive-in. And he doesn't even know what hamburgers are like. So this just shows you the standard of things in Macao.

35 Cyril's surprise —or Home, Sweet Home!

I TOLD you once before what Adam said to Eve about all good things come to an end. Well, Dad says to Mum, Time you get used to the idea of being a Hausfrau again, old girl. Home, sweet home. Mum sighs, eating her last breakfast in bed in Hong Kong. And soon we pack and are off again.

All the way home on the plane I keep wondering if Granny has remembered to bring in my bike. I left it outside in the backyard a year ago. And about Cyril, our cat. You can't leave Cyril alone for such a long time, he could get into bad company. Granny wrote to Hong Kong to say that Cyril brought a wife home and when we get back there will be a big surprise for us. I hope she means she got us a TV.

I think we are in Melbourne when the plane comes down and find it surprisingly hot. Also full of mosquitoes. And men walking around the place with embroidered shirts hanging outside their trousers, which Dad says is the latest touch of fashion. Mum says, It might be in Manila, which is a way to stop Dad from buying one for himself. And this is how I learn that we aren't in Melbourne yet.

We get dinner in the Hotel Manila, six courses and frozen mutton from Australia as a delicacy. Fried mosquitoes no extra charge. The last minute, just as the bus is leaving for the airport, Dad decides to buy this box of cigars, because he has forgotten to take back something for his bank manager. He has this pack of playing-cards to give away, you see, but the bank manager may not appreciate them when he turns them around. On the back of them are lovely naked ladies,

all different shapes. Fifty-two of them for two dollars, Hong Kong money.

We fly all night, and for breakfast we land at Darwin. Dad says we are back in Australia. Time for a kipper and some fish-and-chips, he says. In Darwin they have special à la carte kippers and fish-and-chips to boost English migration to our country.

And soon after breakfast we go and do a bit more flying, and then we are home. In Melbourne, that is. ·

Nothing changed much at home since we left. Granny is still feudal, and she receives us with ischlers and a dobos torte. And on Dad's desk, neatly laid out, there are three hundred and sixty-five bills, one for each day we have been away.

The surprise is Cyril's family. Nine of them, and all part orphans. The mother died, and now Cyril has to look after his children, because he's a widower. Which is why we cannot afford this TV I wanted so much. I knew it all the time, I just did. They promise you the earth, your Mum and Dad do, and say if you'll come along on this trip around the world and behave yourself, you'll get a big surprise when we get home.

Yes. Nine kittens. Always the same.